Aeronautical Knowledge – Air Law

Jeremy M Pratt

ISBN 9781906559717

Published by:
Airplan Flight Equipment Ltd

This book is intended to be a guide to the 2015 EASA Air Law Theoretical Knowledge syllabus for the Private Pilot Licence (PPL) and Light Aircraft Pilot Licence (LAPL) for both aeroplanes and helicopters.

This book is not intended to be an authoritative document and it does not in any way over-rule or counter instruction from an approved or registered training organisation or information or guidance produced by the European Aviation Safety Agency (EASA) or by a Competent Authority. Full reference should be made to applicable EU regulations, EASA Implementing Regulations and EASA Acceptable Means of Compliance and Guidance Material (AMC/GM). Rules, procedures, limitations and guidance in documents produced by Competent Authorities, including but not limited to national law and guidance, Aeronautical Information Publications (AIP), Aeronautical Information Circulars (AIC) and the applicable Aircraft Flight Manual (AFM) – alternatively the Pilots Operating Handbook / Flight Manual (POH/FM) – must also be complied with at all times. Requirements of the aircraft operator, for example in an Operations Manual or flying order book, must also be complied with.

Aeronautical information, including that relating to Air Law, can – and does – change frequently and it is the pilot's responsibility to remain up-to-date with such changes. The provisions of good airmanship and safe operating practice should be adhered to at all times.

Whilst every care has been taken in compiling this publication, relying where possible on authoritative and official information sources, the publisher and editorial team will not be liable in any way for any errors or omission whatsoever.

First edition 2016

Aeronautical Knowledge – Air Law

ISBN 9781906559717

Printed by <?>

Airplan Flight Equipment Ltd
1a Ringway Trading Estate,
Shadowmoss Road,
Manchester M22 5LH UK

www.afeonline.com

Contents

AL7 Air Traffic Services

AL8 Aeronautical Information Service (AIS)

AL9 Urgency and Distress Procedures

AL10 Pilot Licensing

AL11 National Procedures

Foreword

This publication is designed to provide Theoretical Knowledge (TK) in regard to air law for non-commercial flight operations under Visual Flight Rules (VFR). It is based on the 2015 EASA PPL and LAPL Theoretical Knowledge (TK) Air Law syllabus and it is considered suitable for use in conjunction with training courses for the following pilot licences:

- EASA Private Pilot Licence (PPL) (Aeroplane and Helicopter)
- EASA Light Aircraft Pilot Licence (LAPL) (Aeroplane and Helicopter)
- UK National PPL (NPPL)
- ICAO-compliant PPL or equivalent licence
- Core knowledge for EASA Commercial Pilot Licence (CPL)
- Foundation knowledge for EASA Airline Transport Pilot Licence (ATPL)
- Foundation knowledge for EASA Multi-crew Pilot Licence (MPL)

This publication also provides foundation knowledge for an Air Transport Operations/Management degree or similar academic qualification.

About the Author

Jeremy M Pratt took his first flying lesson at the age of 14, paid for by working in the hangar and radio unit at his local airfield. He gained his pilot's licence shortly after his 18th birthday after being awarded an Esso/Air League Flying Scholarship, became a flying instructor at 19 and a commercial pilot at the age of 20.

Since then Jeremy M Pratt has taught (and continues to teach) pilots for a wide range of licences - both private and professional - as well as associated ratings and qualifications including night, instrument, tailwheel and multi-engine flying and has flown General Aviation aircraft professionally in a number of other roles including pleasure flights, traffic reporting, photography and aerial survey. He has owned and co-owned a number of General Aviation aircraft and flown a variety of aircraft types from Tiger Moth biplane to Cessna Citation jet, as well as trying-out helicopter, glider, microlight and balloon flying.

The author's first flying training books were published in 1992, since then they have sold hundreds of thousands of copies world-wide and been translated into a number of languages. In-all Jeremy M Pratt has authored and co-authored around 25 aviation training books as well as contributing to various aviation publications including Flight Training News (FTN), for which he flight tests various aircraft types.

The author works with various aviation authorities and organisations on training and safety issues. Jeremy M Pratt was part of the team that produced the 2015 EASA PPL and LAPL syllabi, he also sits on the CAA's PPL Theoretical Knowledge Working Group. He flies whenever he can find the time - for instructing, for business, for pleasure and for the sheer joy of flight.

Image Acknowledgements

Rights are reserved for all images used in this book. Where known the appropriate rights or copyright holder is listed below. In a small number of cases we have been unable to trace the rights holder for an image, in which case it is marked 'ukn' (unknown):

AL1 International Aviation Law

AL1.1 ukn; AL1.2 ukn; AL1.3 ukn; AL1.4 courtesy ICAO; AL1.5 courtesy EASA; AL1.6 © AFE Ltd; AL1.7 Courtesy EASA; AL1.8 Courtesy DGAC; AL1.9 Courtesy CAA; AL1.10 © AFE Ltd

AL2 European Rules of the Air

AL2.1 courtesy EASA; AL2.2 © Paolo Toffanin; AL2.3 © ChrisD600; AL2.4 © AFE Ltd; AL2.5 © AFE Ltd; AL2.6 © AFE Ltd; AL2.7 © AFE Ltd; AL2.8 © AFE Ltd; AL2.9 © AFE Ltd; AL2.10 © AFE Ltd; AL2.11 © AFE Ltd; AL2.12 © AFE Ltd; AL2.13 © Alexandar Lotzov; AL2.14 © AFE Ltd; AL2.15 © AFE Ltd; AL2.16 © AFE Ltd; AL2.17 © Bristolairport.co.uk; AL2.18 © AFE Ltd; AL2.19 © Ruslan Kudrin; AL2.19; AL2.20 © AFE Ltd; AL2.21 © ByeByeTokyo

AL3 Aerodromes

AL3.1 © AFE Ltd; AL3.2 © AFE Ltd; AL3.3 © AFE Ltd; AL3.4 © AFE Ltd; AL3.5 © AFE Ltd; AL3.6 © AFE Ltd; AL3.7 © AFE Ltd; AL3.8 © AFE Ltd; AL3.9 © AFE Ltd; AL3.10 © Jaromir Chalabala; AL3.11 © AFE Ltd; AL3.12 © AFE Ltd; AL3.13 © AFE Ltd; AL3.14 © AFE Ltd; AL3.15 © AFE Ltd; AL3.16 ukn; AL3.17 Courtesy VansAirForce.net; AL3.18 Courtesy UK AIP; AL3.19 © AFE Ltd; AL3.20 © AFE Ltd; AL3.21 © AFE Ltd; AL3.22 ukn; AL3.23 © AFE Ltd; AL3.24 © AFE Ltd; AL3.25 © AFE Ltd; AL3.26 © AFE Ltd; AL3.27 © AFE Ltd; AL3.28 © AFE Ltd; AL3.29 © AFE Ltd; AL3.30 © AFE Ltd; AL3.31 © AFE Ltd AL3.32 © AFE Ltd; AL3.33 © AFE Ltd; AL3.34 © AFE Ltd

AL4 Visual Meteorological Conditions (VMC) and Visual Flight Rules (VFR)

AL4.1 © AFE Ltd; AL4.2 © AFE Ltd; AL4.3 © AFE Ltd; AL4.4 © AFE Ltd; AL4.5 © AFE Ltd; AL4.6 © AFE Ltd; AL4.7 © AFE Ltd; AL4.8 © AFE Ltd; AL4.9 © AFE Ltd; AL4.10 © AFE Ltd; AL4.11 © AFE Ltd; AL4.12 © AFE Ltd; AL4.13 © AFE Ltd; AL4.14 © AFE Ltd; AL4.15 © AFE Ltd; AL4.16 © tamergunal; AL4.17 © AFE Ltd; AL4.18 © AFE Ltd

AL5 Airspace Classifications

AL5.1 © AFE Ltd; AL5.2 © AFE Ltd; AL5.3 © AFE Ltd; AL5.4 © AFE Ltd; AL5.5 © AFE Ltd; AL5.6 © AFE Ltd; AL5.7 courtesy AIP; AL5.8 courtesy AIP; AL5.9 © AFE Ltd; AL5.10 © Crown Copyright; AL5.11 courtesy AIP; AL5.12 courtesy AIP; AL5.13 courtesy AIP; AL5.14 ukn; AL5.15 © AFE Ltd; AL5.16 ukn; AL5.17 courtesy AIP; AL5.18 courtesy AIP; AL5.19 ukn; AL5.20 courtesy AIP; AL5.21 courtesy AIP; AL5.22 © Crown Copyright; AL5.23 courtesy AIP; AL5.24 courtesy AIP; AL5.25 © AFE Ltd; AL5.26 © Trig Ltd; AL5.27 © Crown Copyright

AL6 Altimeter Setting Procedures

AL6.1 © AFE Ltd; AL6.2 ukn; AL6.3 © AFE Ltd; AL6.4 © AFE Ltd; AL6.5 © AFE Ltd; AL6.6 © AFE Ltd; AL6.7 © AFE Ltd; AL6.8 © AFE Ltd; AL6.9 © AFE Ltd; AL6.9 © AFE Ltd; AL6.10 © AFE Ltd; AL6.11 © AFE Ltd; AL6.12 © Crown Copyright; AL6.13 © AFE Ltd; AL6.14 © SIA; AL6.15 © AFE Ltd; AL6.16 © AFE Ltd; AL6.17 © AFE Ltd; AL6.18 © AFE Ltd; AL6.19 © Crown Copyright; AL6.20 courtesy AIP; © SIA

AL7 Air Traffic Services

AL7.1 © AFE Ltd; AL7.2 © AFE Ltd; AL7.3 ©Angelo Giampiccolo; AL7.4 © AFE Ltd; AL7.5 © AFE Ltd; AL7.6 © Crown Copyright; AL7.7 © AFE Ltd; AL7.8 ©_irakite

AL8 Aeronautical Information Service (AIS)

AL8.1 © Belgocontrol; AL8.2 © AFE Ltd; AL8.3 courtesy AIP; AL8.4 courtesy AIP; AL8.5 courtesy AIP; AL8.6 courtesy AIP; AL8.7 © AFE Ltd; AL8.8 © AFE Ltd; AL8.9 © AFE Ltd; AL8.10 courtesy AIP

AL9 Urgency and Distress Procedures

AL9.1 ukn; AL9.2 ukn; AL9.3 © Olivier Corneloup; AL9.4 © trig Ltd; AL9.5 © AFE Ltd; AL9.6 Courtesy Airbus; AL9.7 © AFE Ltd; AL9.8 © AFE Ltd; AL9.9 Courtesy defenseimagery.mil; AL9.10 © AFE Ltd; AL9.11 © AFE Ltd

AL10 Pilot Licensing

AL10.1 Courtesy CAA; AL10.2 © AFE Ltd; AL10.3 © AFE Ltd; AL10.4 © AFE Ltd; AL10.5 © mangpor2004; AL10.6 © WojciechBeczynski; AL10.7 © Ponomaryov Vlad; AL10.8 © Chesky; AL10.9 © pavelk729; AL10.10 © topseller; AL10.11 © AFE Ltd; AL10.12 © AFE Ltd; AL10.13 © AFE Ltd; AL10.14 ukn; AL10.15 © mpodrucki; AL10.16 © Nadezda Murmakova; AL10.17 Courtesy Piper; AL10.18 © AFE Ltd; AL10.19 Courtesy Textron Aviation, Inc; AL10.20 Copyright Javier Guerrero; AL10.21 Courtesy Textron Aviation, Inc; AL10.22 © Oleg Belyakov; AL10.23 © AFE; AL10.24 © AFE; AL10.25 © Andres Meneses; AL10.26 ukn; AL10.27 ukn; AL10.28 ukn; AL10.29 © AFE; AL10.30 © AFE; AL10.31 Courtesy Piper Aircraft; AL10.32 ukn; AL10.33 ukn; AL10.34 © Chris Procter; AL10.35 © AFE; AL10.36 Courtesy Airbus; AL10.37 © Ismael Jorda; AL10.38 © Alain Genève; AL10.39 © Aleksi Hamalainen; AL10.40 © Danish Aviation Photo

AL11 National Procedures

AL11.1 © CAA, AL11.2 © Javier Guerrero; AL11.3 © AFE Ltd; AL11.4 © AFE Ltd; AL11.5 © AFE Ltd; AL11.6 © AFE; AL11.7 © AFE; AL11.8 © AFE; AL11.9 © Simon Willson; AL11.10 © Crown Copyright; AL11.11 Courtesy National Air Traffic Services; AL11.12 © AFE; AL11.13 Courtesy National Air Traffic Services; AL11.14 © AFE; AL11.15 © Crown Copyright; AL11.16 Courtesy MOD; AL11.17 © AFE; AL11.18 © AFE; AL11.19 Courtesy National Air Traffic Services; AL11.20 © Crown Copyright; AL11.21 Courtesy National Air Traffic Services; AL11.22 Courtesy National Air Traffic Services; AL11.23 © Ron Kellenaers; AL11.24 Courtesy National Air Traffic Services; AL11.25 Courtesy National Air Traffic Services; AL11.26 © Darryl Morrell; AL11.27 Courtesy National Air Traffic Services; AL11.28 © AFE Ltd; AL11.29 © AFE Ltd; AL11.30 Courtesy National Air Traffic Services; AL11.31 Courtesy National Air Traffic Services; AL11.32 Courtesy National Air Traffic Services; AL11.33 © AFE Ltd

Acknowledgements

Creating a book is, rather like flying itself, an activity that needs the help and assistance of a whole range of people to bring the dream into reality. I have been fortunate over the years to have met, flown and worked with a range of very talented people in both the aviation and publishing worlds and many of them have, in one way or another, contributed to this book. The following are just some of the people and organisations who have directly contributed or worked on this book, and I offer my heartfelt thanks to them. To any person or organisation I may have inadvertently missed out, I additionally offer my apologies for the oversight.

Airplan Flight Equipment (AFE)

Air Team Images

Wendy Barratt

Civil Aviation Authority

Crécy Publishing

Flight Training News

Brighton City Airport

Rob Taylor – GDi Studio

Civil Aviation Authority

National Air Traffic Services

Dave Unwin

And, of course, my long-suffering family who continue to put-up with my business trips away, late evenings in the office and working weekends for reasons I've never fully understood.

I fly because it releases my mind from the tyranny of petty things
Antoine de Saint-Exupery

Introduction

'Oh no – not law!'

It's hardly an unexpected reaction. For any pilot, maybe at the beginning of their flying career and experiencing the thrill of flying an aircraft for the first time, the prospect of dredging through boring legislation and solemn legal documents in order to assimilate a collection of phrases and lists of definitions - that you may never use in real-life - is hardly an enticing one.

Fortunately, the reality is rather different.

This book on Air Law has been prepared in-line with the 2015 EASA PPL and LAPL syllabi which the author was involved in creating. The driving force behind these new syllabi was to strip-out purely academic topics from the old syllabi that had little or no application in the real world of non-commercial, Visual Flight Rules (VFR) flight; and instead focus on the real-world knowledge a pilot needs to operate safely and efficiently in day-to-day flying situations.

Thus, the knowledge of air law that this publication encompasses is tied-in to practical situations that any pilot can relate to – for example actions before flight, taxiway markings, how to avoid runway incursion, rights of way in flight, minimum weather conditions, procedures for flying in different types of airspace, medical requirements etc. Armed with this knowledge, a pilot is much better placed to make good decisions and get the best from their pilot's licence. Too often, for example, pilots seem afraid to cross controlled airspace – almost certainly because they have a poor knowledge of the procedures required. Instead, they divert dozens of miles out of their way, maybe 'funnelling' into relatively narrow gaps between controlled airfields and not talking to anyone. Meantime, a more proficient pilot obtains a crossing clearance and enjoys not only enhanced safety and convenience, but often a great close-up view of a major airport in action and increased confidence in their own capabilities.

Even so, sometimes the procedures and regulations of flight can seem inconvenient when they stand in the way of something a pilot really wants to do. There may be a temptation to ignore an awkward rule – especially if the pilot judges that there is little chance of getting caught. At such a time, it is worth remembering that much of aviation law has been developed through so-called 'tombstone legislation' – rules and procedures introduced in reaction to accidents or safety failings which have cost precious lives. There is an aviation adage worth knowing, sometimes attributed to a WWI pilot:

'The rules are there for the guidance of the wise, and the protection of the foolish.'

A final thought about air law. More than any other aspect of aeronautical knowledge, air law changes and is updated frequently. This is particularly true in Europe where national rules and procedures are being replaced with European legislation. In return for the freedom of flight that a pilot enjoys, there is a responsibility to stay up-to-date with the current procedures, not only for the pilot's own safety, but also that of the pilot's passengers, other airspace users and the general public. A little effort spent keeping informed of the latest changes and developments is a small price to pay for the rare privilege of being a pilot.

Jeremy M Pratt
August 2016

AL1 International Aviation Law

International Civil Aviation Organisation (ICAO)

European Aviation Safety Agency (EASA)

National Aviation Authorities

AL1 International Aviation Law

International Civil Aviation Organisation (ICAO)

Figure AL1.1
Signing The Convention on International Civil Aviation in 1944. A spectator sport, apparently.

According to legend, the world's first aviation regulation dates back to Paris in the 1780s. At that time the French Montgolfier brothers were experimenting with hot air balloons, which are credited with making some of the earliest flights to successfully carry humans aloft. It is said that this remarkable feat was quickly followed by the world's first aviation regulation – a local law banning hot air ballooning on a Sunday.

Fast forward to the first half of the 20th century and the potential for powered aircraft to revolutionise international travel soon became apparent, with the first scheduled international flights starting as early as 1919. Regulation of this fast growing industry was disorganised at first, with basic rules often borrowed from an older form of international transport – the maritime world. Aviation legislation developed haphazardly, with each country making up its own flying rules, often implemented in response to the growth of this new industry or a particularly bad accident.

By 1944 it was clear that international civil air transport was likely to boom in a peace-time world, and in that year representatives from 52 countries gathered in Chicago, USA to draw up a document called the 'The Convention on International Civil Aviation', also sometimes known as the 'Chicago Convention'. The convention set out a series of articles to be the guiding principles for developing international aviation rules and the most important of these articles survive to this day:

Article 1 – Sovereignty
Every state (ie country) has complete and exclusive sovereignty over airspace above its territory.

Article 2 – Territory
The territory of a state are the land areas and adjacent territorial waters under the sovereignty, protection or mandate of the state.

Article 5 – Non-Scheduled Flights Over State's Territory
The aircraft of states, other than scheduled international air services, have the right to make flights across state's territories and to make stops without obtaining prior permission.

Article 10 – Landing at Customs Airports
If a state requires crossing aircraft to make a landing, the state can require that landing to be at a designated customs airport. Similarly departure from the territory can be required to be from a designated customs airport.

Article 11 – Applicability of Air Regulations
The laws and regulations of a state applicable to the arrival and departure of aircraft engaged in international air navigation, or to the operation of such aircraft while within its territory, shall apply to the aircraft of all contracting states.

by the State and transmitted to the International Civil Aviation Organization established under Part II of this Convention for communication to all other contracting States.

Article 11

Applicability of air regulations

Subject to the provisions of this Convention, the laws and regulations of a contracting State relating to the admission to or departure from its territory of aircraft engaged in international air navigation, or to the operation and navigation of such aircraft while within its territory, shall be applied to the aircraft of all contracting States without distinction as to nationality, and shall be complied with by such aircraft upon entering or departing from or while within the territory of that State.

Article 12

Rules of the air

Each contracting State undertakes to adopt measures to insure that every aircraft flying over or maneuvering within its territory and that every aircraft carrying its nationality mark, wherever such aircraft may be, shall comply with the rules and regulations relating to the flight and maneuver of aircraft there in force. Each contracting State undertakes to keep its own regulations in these respects uniform, to the greatest possible extent, with those established from time to time under this Convention. Over the high seas, the rules in force shall be those established under this Convention. Each contracting State

Figure AL1.2
An extract from the original version of the Chicago Convention.

Article 12 – Rules of the Air
Every aircraft flying over a state's territory, and every aircraft carrying a territory's nationality mark – wherever it is – must comply with that territory's rules of the air. Each state shall keep its own rules of the air as uniform as possible with those established under the convention, the duty to ensure compliance with these rules rests with the contracting state. Over the high seas, the rules established under the Convention apply.

Article 13 – Entry and Clearance Regulations
A state's laws and regulations regarding the admission and departure of passengers, crew or cargo from aircraft shall be complied with on arrival, upon departure and whilst within the territory of that state.

Article 16 – Search of Aircraft
The authorities of each state shall have the right to search the aircraft of other states on landing or departure, without unreasonable delay, and to inspect certificates and other documents prescribed by this Convention.

Article 17 – Nationality of Aircraft
Aircraft have the nationality of the State in which they registered.

Article 18 – Dual Registration
An aircraft cannot be validly registered in more than one State, but its registration may be changed from one State to another.

Article 20 – Display of Marks
Every aircraft engaged in international air navigation shall bear its appropriate nationality and registration marks.

Article 23 – Customs and Immigration Procedures
Each state undertakes to establish customs and immigration procedures affecting international air navigation in accordance with the practices established by the Convention.

Article 24 – Customs Duty
Aircraft flying to, from, or across the territory of a state shall be admitted temporarily free of duty. Fuel, oil, spare parts, regular equipment and aircraft stores retained on board are also exempt customs duty, inspection fees or similar charges.

Article 29 – Documents Carried in Aircraft
Every aircraft engaged in international navigation shall carry the following documents:

- Its Certificate of Registration
- Its Certificate of Airworthiness
- Crew licences
- Journey logbook
- Radio licence
- A list of passenger names, places of embarkation and destination
- A cargo manifest

Note: It is an international standard that before an international flight, the Pilot-In-Command must ensure that the aircraft is airworthy, that it is duly registered and that all relevant certificates are on board the aircraft.

Article 30 – Aircraft Radio Equipment
Aircraft of a state flying in or over the territory of another state shall only carry radios licensed and used in accordance with the regulations of the state in which the aircraft is registered. The radio(s) may only be used by members of the flight crew issued with a licence for that purpose by the state in which the aircraft is registered.

Article 31 – Certificates of Airworthiness
Every aircraft engaged in international navigation must have a valid Certificate of Airworthiness issued by the state in which it is registered.

Article 32 – Licences of Personnel
The pilot and crew of aircraft engaged in international navigation must have certificates of competency and licences issued or validated by the state in which the aircraft is registered. For the purposes of flight over its own territory, each state reserves the right to refuse to recognise certificates of competency or licences granted to any of its nationals by another state.

Article 33 – Recognition of Certificates and Licences
Certificates of Airworthiness, certificates of competency and licences issued or validated by the state in which the aircraft is registered, shall be recognised as valid by other states. The requirements for issue of those Certificates of Airworthiness, certificates of competency and licences must be equal to or above the minimum standards established by the Convention.

Article 34 – Journey Logbooks
Every aircraft engaged in international navigation will have a journey logbook which must be maintained with details of the aircraft, its crew and each journey.

Article 35 – Cargo Restrictions
No munitions or implements of war may be carried in or over the territory of a state except with the permission of that state.

Article 37 – Adoption of International Standards and Procedures
Each state shall collaborate in securing the highest practical uniformity in air navigation;

regulations, standards, procedures and organisation in relation to aircraft; personnel; airways and auxiliary services.

Article 39 – Endorsement of Certificates and Licenses
An aircraft or part which fails to satisfy an international standard of airworthiness or performance, shall have endorsed on or attached to its airworthiness certificate complete details regarding that failure. Any licence holder who does not satisfy international standards shall have attached to or endorsed on their licence information regarding the particulars in which they do not satisfy those standards.

Article 40 – Validity of Endorsed Certificates and Licenses
No aircraft or personnel with endorsed licences or certificates shall engage in international navigation except with the permission of the state or states whose territory is entered.

It is important to stress that these articles are principles only, they do not constitute law and whilst they are used to guide aviation rules and regulations, in the real world they are rarely adopted into aviation legislation in every state without some modification or exceptions.

The convention also set up the **International Civil Aviation Organisation – ICAO** – which had the remit to develop international Standards and Recommended Practices (SARPs). ICAO, which is an agency of the United Nations (UN), now has 191 member states and has developed well over 10,000 SARPs. The principles for these standards and recommendations are established in a series of 'annexes', each covering a particular aspect of aviation law, regulation or procedure. These annexes include:

Figure AL1.3
ICAO headquarters in Montreal, Canada.

Annex 1	Personnel Licensing
Annex 2	Rules of the Air
Annex 3	Meteorological Services for International Air Navigation
Annex 6	Operation of Aircraft
Annex 7	Aircraft Nationality and Registration Marks
Annex 8	Airworthiness of Aircraft
Annex 9	Facilitation
Annex 11	Air Traffic Services
Annex 12	Search and Rescue Services
Annex 13	Aircraft Accident Investigation
Annex 14	Aerodromes
Annex 15	Aeronautical Information Services
Annex 17	Security
Annex 18	Transport of Dangerous Goods by Air
Annex 19	Safety Management

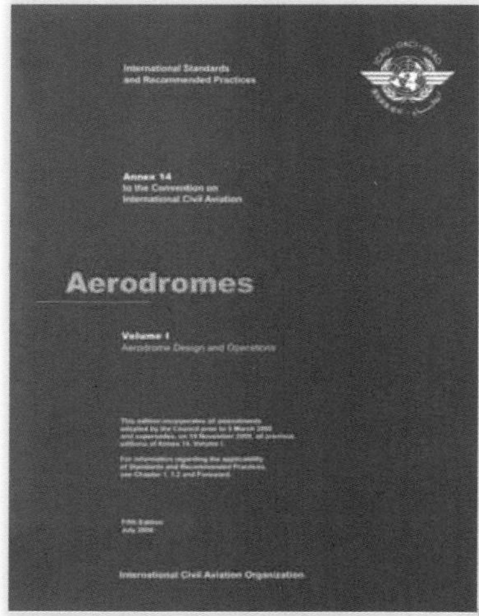

Figure AL1.4
ICAO Annex 14 – Aerodromes.

Although individual States can establish their own rules and procedures, in practice these are usually based closely on ICAO standards and recommendations. Where a country has rules or procedures that differ from an ICAO standard, the state will usually publish a list of those differences from ICAO standards and recommendations.

European Aviation Safety Agency (EASA)

Figure AL1.5
The European Aviation Safety Agency (EASA) is the European Union (EU) authority for aviation safety.

The **European Aviation Safety Agency** (**EASA**) is the European Union (EU) authority for aviation safety. Established in 2002, EASA develops common aviation safety rules and procedures at European level and it monitors the implementation of these standards by the member states. EASA currently has 32 member states – not all of which are EU members. Once EASA rules are put into EU regulation, the member states are largely required to adopt those regulations into their own national law, with limited options to modify the regulations (although a member state may use a 'derogation' to delay the implementation of an element of an EU regulation into their own national legal system).

Figure AL1.6
The member states of EASA.

European Aviation Safety Agency

Acceptable Means of Compliance and Guidance Material to Part-FCL[1]

Figure AL1.7
The Acceptable Means of Compliance and Guidance Material (AMC/GM) for the Flight Crew Licencing (FCL) regulations, as published by EASA.

The key areas in which EASA regulations affect the daily life of pilots includes aircraft certification and maintenance, Flight Crew Licencing (FCL), training standards, aircraft operation, Air Traffic Management and airports. EU regulations are written by lawyers rather than pilots, and the practical application of these regulations is not a matter for EASA, but is expected to be carried out by each individual state's own aviation authority.

EASA regulations are published as **Implementing Regulations** (sometimes called 'hard law'), which are legal requirements issued in the form of an EU Commission Regulation. Explanations for these Implementing Regulations, offering further detail and guidance about how they should be applied in practice, are published by EASA in the form of **Acceptable Means of Compliance and Guidance Material** (**AMC/GM**) which are sometimes called 'soft law'.

Figure AL1.8
Each NAA is responsible for applying EASA rules on civil aviation within their state, for example the DGAC is responsible for aviation matters in France.

National Aviation Authorities (NAA)

National Aviation Authority (**NAA**) is a general term for the organisation which enforces aviation rules and procedures within a specific state. The NAA is often a government department which issues pilot licences and ratings, registers aircraft, promotes aviation safety and, when necessary, takes action against those who break the law. Each EASA member state has its own NAA and each NAA has a different name (often known by its initials, because aviation is full of abbreviations and acronyms). For example in France there is the 'Direction Generale de l'Aviation Civile' (DGAC); in Germany there is the 'Bundesministeriums fur Verkehr, Bau und Stadtentwicklung' (BMVBS); the United Kingdom has the 'Civil Aviation Authority' (CAA).

The NAAs have responsibility for making sure that EASA regulations are applied at national level. This means that despite the best efforts of EASA and the EU law makers, there may be variations across the EASA member states in how EASA regulations are interpreted and administered. Nevertheless, when a pilot needs guidance on a matter of aviation law, it is the appropriate NAA which should be expected to provide the definitive answer. An NAA is sometimes referred to as the **competent authority** for the state it represents. According to EU definition, a competent authority is the authority designated by the member state as competent to ensure compliance with the requirements of an EU regulation.

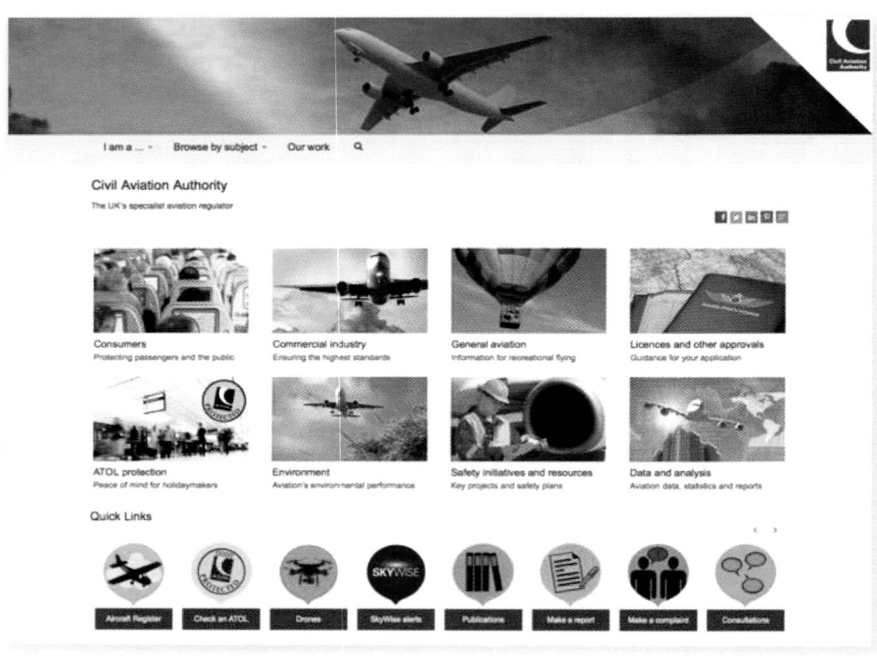

Figure AL1.9
Most NAA's have reasonably informative websites, in this case the UK CAA.

Figure AL1.10
The organisation of international aviation law.

Progress Check

1. Are ICAO SARPS mandatory law in an ICAO member state?
2. What is an EASA 'Acceptable Means of Compliance and Guidance Material' (AMC/GM)?
3. What is the meaning of a 'competent authority'.

These questions are intended to test knowledge and reinforce some of the key learning points from this section. In answering these questions, a 'pass rate' of around 80% should be the target.

Model answers are found at page 143

AL2 European Rules of the Air

Applicability and Compliance

Pilot In Command Responsibilities

Pre-flight Actions

Avoidance of Collisions and Rights of Way

Operation in the Vicinity of an Aerodrome

AL2 European Rules of the Air

Applicability and Compliance

The European rules of the air are established by EU regulation and commonly known as the **Standardised European Rules of the Air** – or **SERA**. These European rules are closely based on ICAO recommendations and in particular ICAO Annex 2 (Rules of the Air).

The Standardised European Rules of the Air (SERA) apply to:

- airspace users and aircraft operating into, within, or out of the European Union;
- airspace users and aircraft carrying the nationality and registration marks of a Member State of the European Union.

Where an EU registered aircraft is operating outside the EU, these rules of the air still apply unless they conflict with the rules of the state whose territory is being overflown. Over the 'high seas', the rules in ICAO Annex 2 apply ('high seas airspace' means airspace beyond land territory and territorial seas). The Standardised European Rules of the Air also apply to the relevant ground personnel engaged in aircraft operations.

Member states are obliged to ensure compliance with the Standardised European Rules of the Air within their state, although in practical terms compliance during a flight is the responsibility of the Pilot In Command.

Figure AL2.1
An extract from the EU Regulation known as the Standardised European Rules of the Air – SERA.

Pilot In Command Responsibilities

The **Pilot-In-Command** is a legally defined term under SERA, it means the pilot designated by the aircraft operator or owner as being in command and charged with the safe conduct of a flight. However, these dry legal words do not do full justice to the responsibility placed upon the pilot of even the smallest aircraft.

A Pilot In Command (**PIC**), and anyone who aspires to be a Pilot In Command, must accept from the very beginning that the operation of the aircraft they are responsible for carries with it the possibility of causing serious harm not only to the occupants of the aircraft itself, but also to other airspace users and even the general public. This responsibility is particularly evident when carrying passengers who, by definition, entrust their safety entirely to the skill and judgement of their pilot. It is a regrettable feature of many present-day cultures that when things go wrong, those responsible may be quick to deny blame or seek to excuse their actions as unavoidable. The laws of gravity are no respecter of the desire to avoid blame or liability and the laws of aviation are themselves often legislated as criminal law, with serious penalties for those who contravene.

So, every pilot must understand that if they ask the question, *"Who is responsible for the safety of this flight?"*, the only possible answer must be *"I am"*.

The term Pilot In Command applies equally to the pilot of the smallest single engine aircraft, as to the pilot of the largest airliner. Where an aircraft carries more than one pilot, it is important to understand that the PIC is not necessarily the pilot actually flying the aircraft or handling the controls at any given moment. Sometimes it should be obvious who the PIC is – for example when an instructor and student pilot fly together during a flying lesson. At other times, for example when co-owners of an aircraft fly together, it is

Figure AL2.2
The Pilot In Command is the one person who carries the ultimate responsibility for the safety of the flight.

necessary to agree before flight who is taking the role of PIC. It is also important to understand that a PIC cannot delegate their responsibilities to others. If a pilot chooses, for example, to let someone else refuel the aircraft, it is still the PIC who is responsible for ensuring that the correct amount and grade of fuel goes into the correct tanks.

Flight safety is heavily reliant on the quality of decisions taken by the PIC. It is the purpose of aviation regulations to give the PIC a framework of rules and guidance of good practice in order to make safe and sensible decisions and to avoid risky or dangerous situations.

The pilot-in-command of an aircraft is responsible for operating the aircraft in accordance with the rules of SERA, although the PIC *"may depart from these rules in circumstances that render such departure absolutely necessary in the interests of safety."* To establish the right of the PIC to take the decisions necessary to ensure flight safety, SERA emphasises that the pilot-in-command of an aircraft has the final authority over the operation of the aircraft. In other words, the PIC is in charge, with all the authority – and responsibility – that involves. To underline the point, SERA is very specific about the safe operation of an aircraft, *"An aircraft shall not be operated in a negligent or reckless manner so as to endanger life or property of others."*

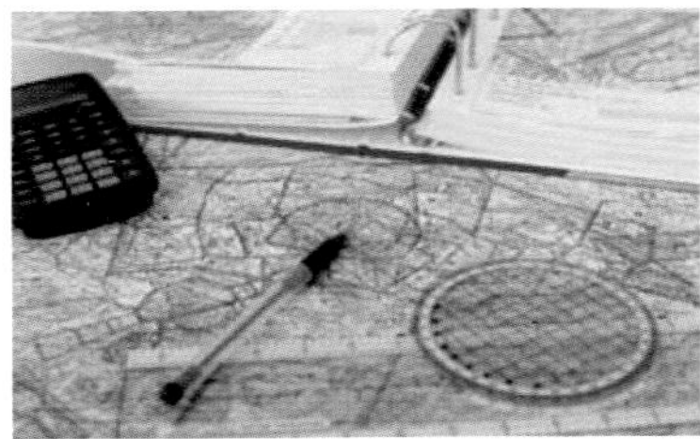

Figure AL2.3
The Pilot In Command is responsible for ensuring that appropriate pre-flight actions have been properly completed – this invariably involves an element of planning for the intended flight.

Pre-flight Actions

Many of the most important decisions and actions that determine the safe conduct of a flight are taken by a PIC before even reaching the aircraft. Factors such as weather, aircraft serviceability, fuel load etc. will all influence the safety of a flight. It is the duty of the PIC to take these factors into account and make the decisions, and take the necessary precautions and actions, to ensure the safety of the flight. SERA specifically requires that before flight, the PIC must consider *"...all available information appropriate to the intended operation"*. Where a flight is leaving the vicinity of an airfield, SERA specifically requires that the PIC shall:

- Make a careful study of available current weather reports and forecasts;
- Take into consideration fuel requirements; and
- Consider an alternative course of action if the flight cannot be completed as planned.

Figure AL2.4
Aircraft must not fly in formation unless the pilots have agreed to do so. Even then, formation flying is not a safe activity unless all the pilots involved are properly trained and prepared.

Avoidance of Collisions and Rights of Way

Regardless of anything written in any aviation rule or regulation, ultimately it is the PIC who is responsible for taking whatever action is necessary, including collision avoidance manoeuvres, to best avoid a collision. Anyone who has travelled on public roads will know that occasionally it is necessary to 'give way' to avoid a dangerous situation, even when you technically have right of way. The same principle applies in the air, although such situations are much rarer than on the roads.

There is an over-riding principle that an aircraft shall not fly so close to another aircraft as to create the danger of a collision. Additionally, aircraft are only permitted to fly in formation if this has been pre-arranged by the PICs of the participating aircraft. There are further rules that apply to formation flying, but these are the concern of those with proper training in formation flying, as flying in formation is definitely not an activity for the untrained. Although it can look simple to the casual observer (and can be a lot of fun for properly prepared pilots), formation flying requires appropriate training and regular practice, formation flying is absolutely not a 'have a go' activity. Over the years a number of untrained pilots have proved, sometimes with tragic results, that formation flying is dangerous without the proper training, planning and preparation.

'Right of way' can be defined as the right of a vehicle (such as an aircraft) in a particular situation to proceed with priority over others. If a pilot is aware that another aircraft has right of way, that pilot is required to 'give way' – that is, keep out of the way of the other aircraft and specifically to avoid passing over, under or in front of the other aircraft, unless it is possible to remain well clear of the aircraft with right of way. The aircraft that has right of way should maintain its heading and speed (unless, of course, this would itself create the danger of a collision). If a pilot is aware that another aircraft has impaired (eg reduced) manoeuvrability, the pilot must give way to that aircraft.

The SERA rules for avoiding collisions in flight have provisions for avoiding collision in specific situations.

If two aircraft are approaching '**head-on**' (or approximately 'head-on') and there is a danger of collision, each aircraft must alter its heading **to the right**.

Figure AL2.5
Where aircraft are approaching each other head-on, each must alter course to its right.

If aircraft are **converging**, a rule of precedence applies, meaning that certain classes of aircraft have priority over others. The order of precedence in a converging situation is:

- Balloons
- Sailplanes (eg gliders)
- Airships
- Aircraft towing another aircraft or object
- Power-driven, heavier than air, aircraft

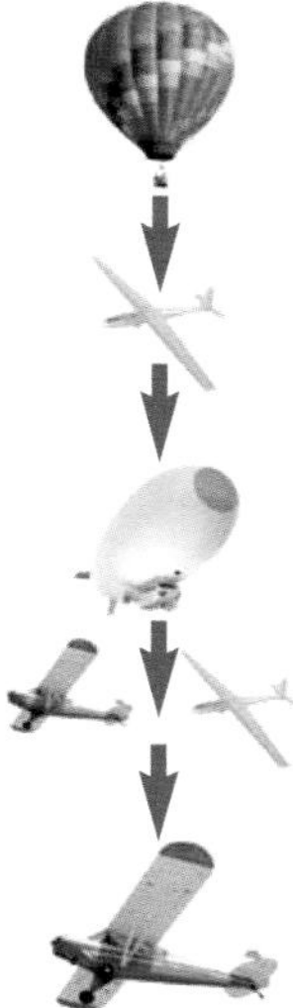

Figure AL2.6
The order of precedence in converging flight. For example, airships give way to sailplanes and balloons, but have priority over aircraft towing another aircraft or object and power-driven, heavier than air, aircraft.

Figure AL2.7
Where two aircraft of equal precedence are converging, the one on the right has right of way – ***"On the right, in the right".***

If the two aircraft converging are of the same class, as defined above, the aircraft that has the other to its right must give way. This rule can be summed up as '**On the Right, In the Right**'.

If an aircraft wishes to **overtake** another aircraft in the air, the aircraft that is being overtaken has right of way and the overtaking aircraft must alter its heading **to the right** to keep clear, whether in climbing, descending or level flight. No subsequent change in the relative positions of the two aircraft absolves the pilot of the overtaking aircraft from the responsibility to keep clear of the other aircraft until well clear and past. An overtaking situation exists whilst the overtaking aircraft is at an angle of 70° or less to the centreline of the aircraft being overtaken.

A sailplane can overtake another sailplane by altering its heading to either right or left.

Figure AL2.8
An overtaking aircraft must alter its heading to the right to keep clear of the other aircraft. The aircraft being overtaken has right-of-way.

Figure AL2.9
An overtaking situation exists while the overtaking aircraft is at an angle of less than 70 degrees to the centre line of the aircraft being overtaken.

Operation in the Vicinity of an Aerodrome

To understand the rules of avoiding collisions on and around aerodromes, it is necessary to know the proper definitions of a few common aviation terms.

Aerodrome	a defined area of land or water intended to be used for the arrival, departure and surface movement of aircraft.
Apron	a defined area intended for aircraft to load or unload, refuel, park, or undergo maintenance.
Controlled aerodrome	an aerodrome at which an Air Traffic Control (ATC) service is provided.
Manoeuvring area	the part of an aerodrome to be used for the take-off, landing and taxiing of aircraft, excluding aprons.
Movement area	the manoeuvring area and the apron(s) of an aerodrome.
Runway	a defined rectangular area on a land aerodrome prepared for the landing and take-off of aircraft.
Runway-holding position	a designated position intended to protect a runway at which taxiing aircraft and vehicles must stop and hold, unless otherwise authorised.
Taxiing	movement of an aircraft on the surface of an aerodrome under its own power, excluding take-off and landing.
Taxiway	a defined path on a land aerodrome established for the taxiing of aircraft.

Figure AL2.10
SERA definitions in relation to aerodromes.

When operating on or in the vicinity of an aerodrome, aircraft must:

- Observe other aerodrome traffic to avoid collision;
- Conform with the traffic pattern formed by other aircraft, or avoid the pattern;
- Make all turns to the left when approaching for a landing and after taking off - unless otherwise indicated, or instructed by Air Traffic Control;
- Land and take-off into the wind unless safety, the runway configuration, or air traffic considerations determine that a different direction is preferable.

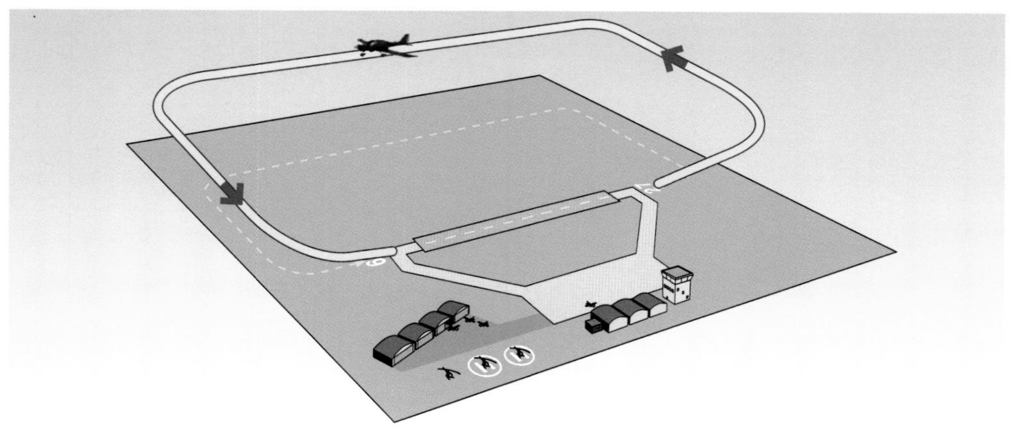

Figure AL2.11
An aircraft in the vicinity of an aerodrome must either conform with the established traffic pattern or stay well clear of it. The traffic pattern (or 'circuit') is usually, but not always, left-hand.

Figure AL2.12
On the approach to land, the lowest aircraft usually has right of way.

Aircraft in the air or on the surface must give way to aircraft landing or in the final stages of an approach to land. When two or more 'heavier-than-air' aircraft are approaching an aerodrome to land, the aircraft at the higher level must give way to the aircraft at the lower level. However, an aircraft at the lower level must not cut in front of another aircraft which is in the final stages of an approach to land, or overtake that aircraft. Powered heavier-than-air aircraft must give way to sailplanes (gliders).

If a pilot is aware that another aircraft is making an emergency landing, that pilot must give way to the emergency aircraft.

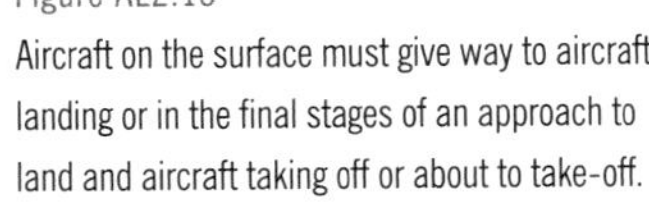

Figure AL2.13
Aircraft on the surface must give way to aircraft landing or in the final stages of an approach to land and aircraft taking off or about to take-off.

An aircraft taxiing on the manoeuvring area of an aerodrome must give way to aircraft taking off or about to take-off.

If there is the danger of collision between two aircraft taxiing on the movement area of an aerodrome, the following rules apply:

When two aircraft are approaching **head on**, or approximately so, each shall **stop** or where practicable alter its course **to the right** to keep well clear;

Figure AL2.14
If two aircraft on the ground are approaching head on, each must stop or where possible alter course to the right.

When two aircraft are on a **converging** course, the one which has the other on its right shall give way (**'On the right, In the right'**);

Figure AL2.15
Where two aircraft are converging on the ground, the one on the right has right of way – ***"On the right, in the right".***

Figure AL2.16
When overtaking on the ground, the overtaking aircraft must keep well clear of the other aircraft.

Figure AL2.17
A lit stop bar at an aerodrome must not be passed.

An aircraft which is being **overtaken** by another aircraft shall have the right-of-way, the overtaking aircraft shall **keep well clear** of the other aircraft.

An aircraft taxiing on the manoeuvring area must stop and hold at all lighted stop bars and may only proceed further in accordance with an Air Traffic Control (ATC) clearance, when the lights are switched off.

Figure AL2.18
A runway holding position or holding point. The designator signs show that this is holding point 'J' for runway 26/08. Note the yellow runway holding point lines across the taxiway and amber 'guard lights' at the sides of the taxiway.

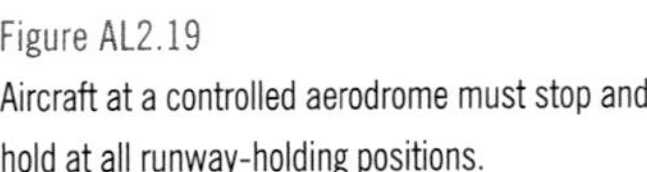

Figure AL2.19
Aircraft at a controlled aerodrome must stop and hold at all runway-holding positions.

An aircraft taxiing on the manoeuvring area of a controlled aerodrome must stop and hold at all runway-holding positions, unless an explicit clearance to enter or cross the runway has been issued by ATC.

On the manoeuvring area:

- Vehicles and vehicles towing aircraft must give way to aircraft which are landing, taking off, or taxiing;
- Vehicles must give way to other vehicles towing aircraft;
- Vehicles and vehicles towing aircraft must comply with instructions issued by ATC.

Emergency vehicles going to the assistance of an aircraft in distress have priority over all other surface movement traffic.

Figure AL2.21
Emergency vehicles going to the assistance of an aircraft in distress have priority over all other surface movement traffic.

Figure AL2.20
Vehicles on the manoeuvring area must give way to aircraft and aircraft being towed.

EASA requires that an aeroplane can only be taxied on the movement area of an aerodrome if the person at the controls is an appropriately qualified pilot; or has been designated by the operator. In either case, the person at the controls must:

- Be trained to taxi the aeroplane;
- Be trained to use the radio, if radio communications are required;
- Have received instruction in respect of aerodrome layout, routes, signs, marking, lights, air traffic control (ATC) signals and instructions, phraseology and procedures; and
- Be able to conform to the operational standards required for safe aeroplane movement at the aerodrome.

Progress Check

4. How can the term Pilot-In-Command best be defined?
5. Under what circumstances (if any) can a PIC deviate from the rules of SERA?
6. Who is responsible for undertaking the pre-flight actions required under SERA?
7. If two aircraft are approaching each other approximately 'head on' in the air, what action should each take?
8. If two aircraft of the 'classification' (as defined in SERA) are converging in the air, what action should each aircraft take?
9. If an aircraft wishes to overtake another aircraft in the air, what action should the overtaking aircraft take?
10. How is an overtaking situation in the air defined?
11. If an aircraft arrives at an aerodrome where an established pattern is being flown, and in the absence of an instruction to the contrary, what action must the arriving aircraft take?
12. If two powered aircraft are approaching to land, and in the absence of an instruction to the contrary, which aircraft has 'priority'?
13. If two aircraft on the ground are approaching each other approximately 'head-on, what action must each aircraft take?
14. If two aircraft are converging on the ground, what action should each aircraft take?
15. If an aircraft wishes to overtake another aircraft on the ground, what action should the overtaking aircraft take?
16. Under what circumstances can an aircraft cross a lit 'stop bar'?
17. If an aircraft is taxiing at a controlled aerodrome, under what circumstances can it pass a runway-holding point?
18. What personnel are permitted to taxi an aircraft on the movement area of an aerodrome?

These questions are intended to test knowledge and reinforce some of the key learning points from this section. In answering these questions, a 'pass rate' of around 80% should be the target.

Model answers are found at page 143

AL3 Aerodromes

Taxiway and Runway Signs and Markings

Preventing Runway Incursion

Other ground signals

Marshalling Signals

Light Signals

AL3 Aerodromes

Taxiway and Runway Signs and Markings

The size and shape of an **aerodrome** (*"a defined area of land or water intended to be used for the arrival, departure and surface movement of aircraft"*) varies, from major international airports to small uncontrolled airstrips. It follows that the surface markings of taxiways and runways also vary from place to place although a pilot can expect that, in general, the bigger and busier the aerodrome, the more comprehensive and sophisticated its taxiway and runway markings will be.

A paved taxiway or apron may have painted markings for the guidance of pilots, these markings should be yellow in colour. The simplest taxiway marking may be a continuous yellow centre-line denoting the middle of the taxiway. Where a taxiway crosses a runway, the taxiway centreline may be interrupted to accommodate the runway markings. There may also be edge markings to indicate the limit of the useable taxiway surface. Taxiways may be identified by a letter – eg taxiway A, taxiway B etc., the taxiway designator may be painted on the taxiway itself. Where a taxiway marking indicates a location (for example, the taxiway designator), the inscription should be yellow on a black background. Where the marking indicates a direction (for example, showing 'this way to taxiway B') the marking should be a black inscription on a yellow background. Taxiway information markings are commonly supplemented or replaced with signs next to the taxiway, which use the same colours as the taxiway markings. A mandatory sign or marking (for example, No Entry') has a white inscription on a red background.

Figure AL3.1
A taxiway centreline marked in yellow.

Figure AL3.2
A taxiway information sign – in this case showing the direction to the refuelling area.

Figure AL3.3
A taxiway information sign showing that this is taxiway 'G', with direction arrows to follow that taxiway.

AL3.4
Taxiway signs with the following meanings:

Taxiway designator

A specific taxiway location

End of taxiway

Figure AL3.5
A mandatory taxiway sign – in this case meaning 'No Entry'

No Entry

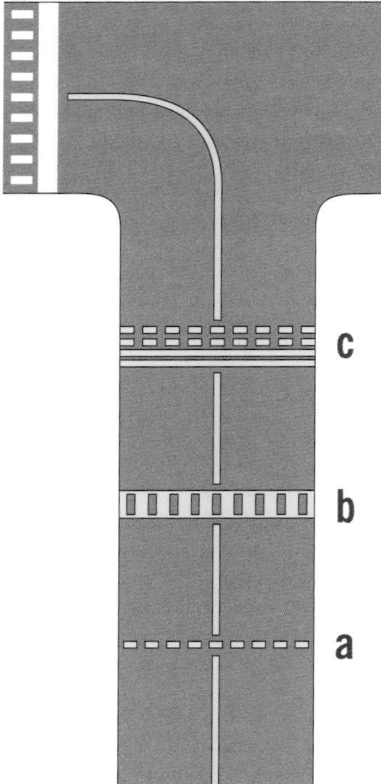

Figure AL3.6
Taxiway holding point markings:
a. An intermediate taxiway holding position.
b. Other taxiway runway holding position, usually associated with Instrument Landing System (ILS) categories and marked 'CAT II' or 'CAT III'.
c. Final taxiway runway holding position (the last holding point on the taxiway before reaching the runway)'

A taxiway may have one or more holding points, for example where another taxiway is crossed or as the taxiway meets a runway. An 'intermediate' taxiway holding point may be marked by a yellow dashed line across the taxiway. An taxiway holding position associated with a runway's Instrument Landing System (ILS) may be marked by so-called 'ladder' markings across the taxiway. Intermediate runway holding positions will normally also be indicated by signs next to the taxiway which indicate the runway designation and the identification of the holding position or location. The final runway holding point may be marked by two solid and two broken lines across the taxiway – the broken lines will be on the 'runway' side of the holding point lines. The runway designation may also be painted on the taxiway itself. The final runway holding point may also be marked by signs at the side of the taxiway and lights beside and/or across the taxiway.

Figure AL3.7
A runway holding point – in this case holding point 'G3' for runway 26/08.

Figure AL3.8
Runway 'guard lights' at a final runway holding point.

Figure AL3.9
Crosses painted on the surface indicate a runway or taxiway (or section of taxiway or runway) which is unfit for the movement of aircraft.

A cross or series of crosses on a taxiway indicates an area which is unfit for the movement of aircraft.

Runway surface markings are painted in white. Most runways have a two-digit runway designator. This designator indicates the runway direction (in degrees referenced to magnetic North) to the nearest 10 degrees, for example a runway designated '24' has a direction of around 240 degree magnetic; a runway designated 05 has a direction of around 050 degrees magnetic. If an airfield has two or more parallel runways, these will be designated as 'L' (left); 'C' (centre) or 'R' (right) as appropriate, so a runway designated '22L' is the left-hand runway with a direction of around 220 degrees magnetic.

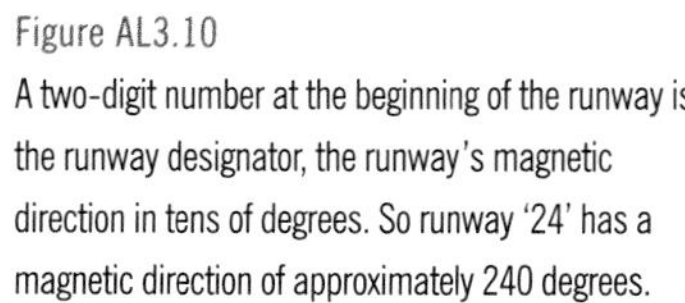

Figure AL3.10
A two-digit number at the beginning of the runway is the runway designator, the runway's magnetic direction in tens of degrees. So runway '24' has a magnetic direction of approximately 240 degrees.

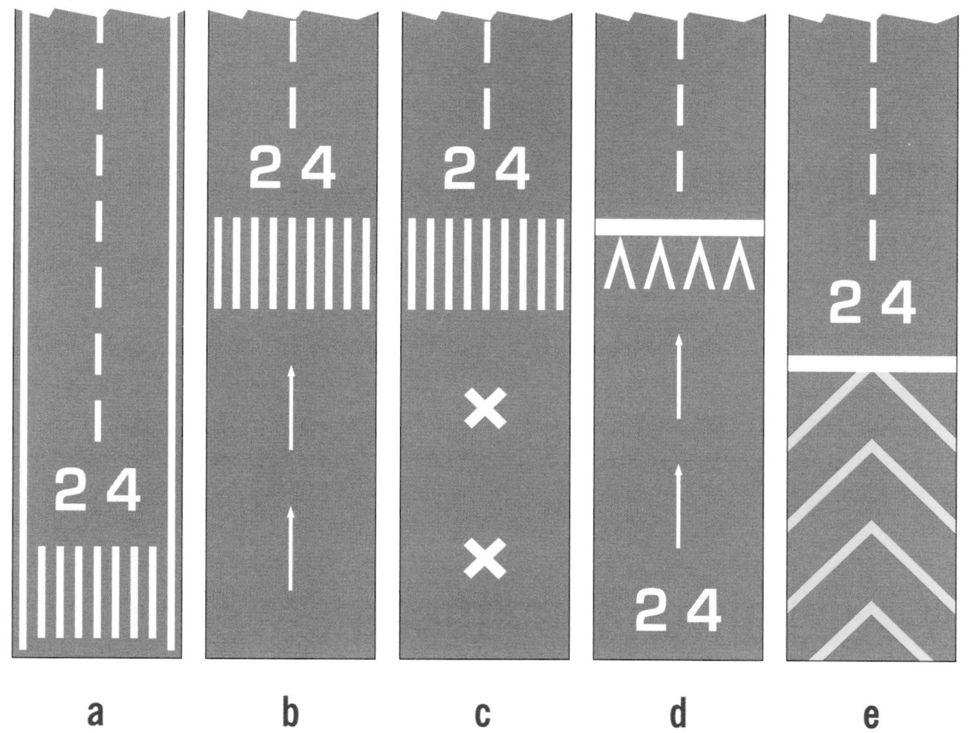

Figure AL3.11
a. Hard runway threshold (sometimes called the 'piano keys'), runway designator, centre line and white edge markings.
b. A 'displaced' runway threshold, on landing the pilot must not land before the threshold. The arrows indicate an area which can be used for take-off, but not for landing.
c. A 'displaced' runway threshold, on landing the pilot must not land before the threshold. The crosses indicate an area which is unfit for any movement of aircraft.
d. A temporarily displaced runway threshold, do not land before the white line after the chevron arrow heads.
e. The yellow chevrons before the runway threshold designate the area as not fit for the normal movement of aircraft.

In addition to the runway designator, the beginning (or 'threshold') of a paved runway may have threshold markings. These often consist of a series of white stripes sometimes known as the 'Piano Keys'. A runway threshold may be 'displaced' – that is the useable portion of the runway does not begin right at the start of the runway surface itself. In this instance the threshold markings will indicate the beginning of the runway usable for landing and there may be a series of pre-threshold arrows on the runway centre-line which mark an area where take-off can be commenced.

A temporary displaced threshold may be indicated by a single line across the runway with small arrowheads against the line.

The runway centre-line may be marked by a dashed white line, and the runway edge may be marked by solid or broken white lines and corner markings.

As with taxiway markings, a series of crosses indicates a portion of runway (or an entire runway) which is unfit for the movement of aircraft.

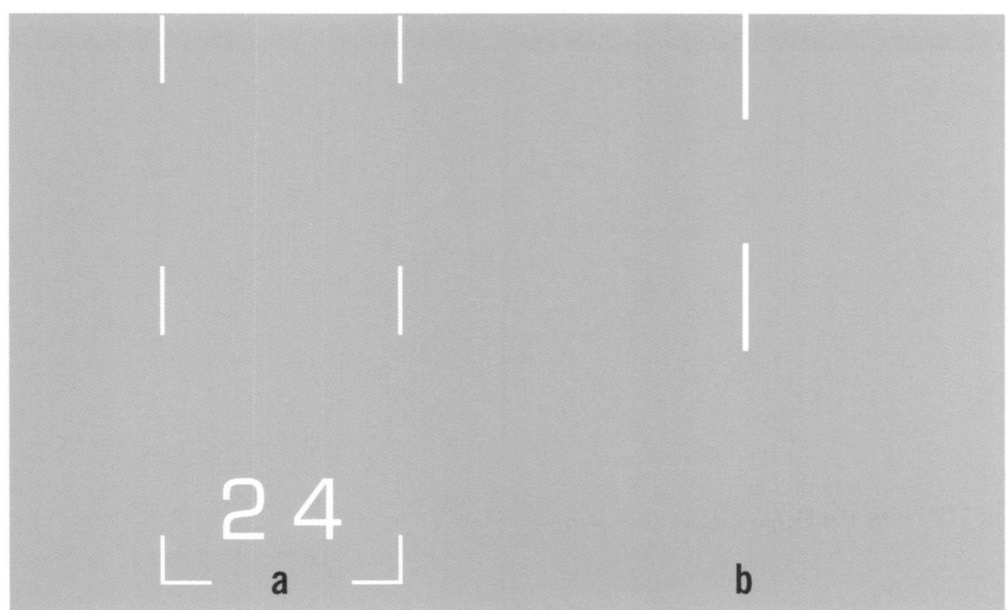

Figure AL3.12
a. Grass runways may be denoted by white 'dashes' at the edges and corners.
b. Grass runways may alternatively be denoted by white centre line markings only.

Figure AL3.13
The start of the runway may be marked by a line of green lights across the runway threshold. A line of red lights may mark the 'stop' end of the runway.

Runways may have one or more lighting systems to guide pilots, in particular when on the approach to land. A line of green lights across the runway indicate the start (threshold) of the runway. A line of red lights indicate the end of the runway.

A runway may also have a light installation to indicate the recommended approach 'glide slope' (the descent path for a landing aircraft). There are three principle types of approach slope indicators:

Precision Approach Path Indicator (PAPI) – a set of four lamp units usually located on the left-hand side of the runway when viewed in the landing direction. When the installation shows two white and two red lights, the aircraft is on the recommended approach slope. Three white lights and one red indicates the aircraft is slightly high, four white lights indicates the aircraft is high. Three red and one white light indicates the aircraft is slightly low, four red lights indicates the aircraft is low.

Abbreviated Precision Approach Path Indicator (APAPI) – a set of two lamps similar to the PAPI system. Both white indicates that the aircraft is high, one white and one red indicates the aircraft is on the correct approach slope. Two red lights indicates the aircraft is low.

Visual Approach Slope Indicator (VASI) – two sets of two lamps each; red lights above white lights indicate the aircraft is on the correct approach slope. All white lights indicate the aircraft is too high, all red indicate the aircraft is too low.

Figure AL3.14
An abbreviated Precision Approach Path Indicator (APAPI) installation.

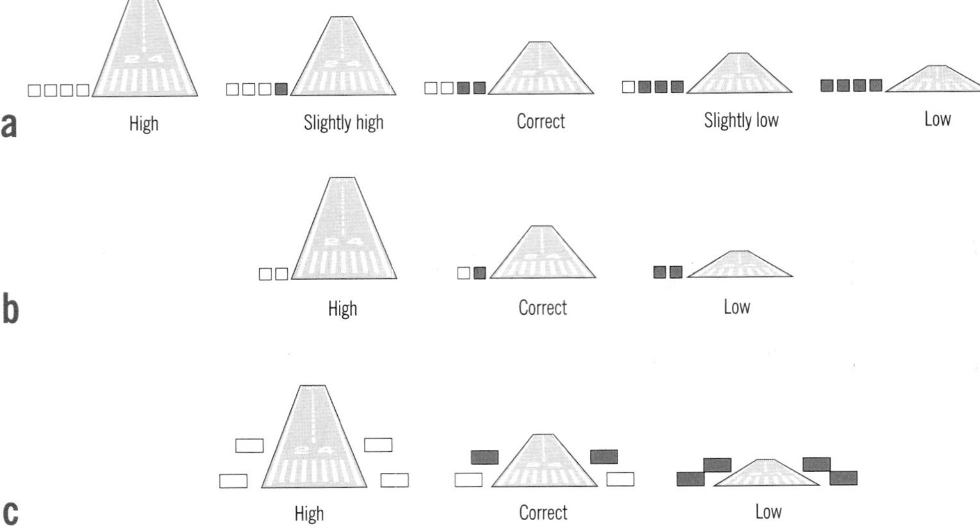

Figure AL3.15
a. A Precision Approach Path Indicator (PAPI) installation is usually found at a runway which has an instrument approach procedure and gives guidance on the recommended vertical profile of the approach.
b. An Abbreviated Precision Approach Path Indicator (APAPI).
c. A Visual Approach Slope Indicator (VASI) installation may be used at some airfields in place of PAPI.

Preventing Runway Incursion

The primary purpose of taxiway and runway markings and signage is to aid navigation on an airfield, and probably the greatest risk associated with ground movement on an airfield is that of 'runway incursion'.

A **'runway incursion'** is a situation where an aircraft (or ground vehicle) is on the runway when it shouldn't be, leading to a risk of collision. At large airports equipped for 'all weather' operations there may be a number of sophisticated systems to prevent runway incursion, including ATC-controlled lighting systems and ground movement radar. At a minor aerodrome there may be no radio, markings or signage at all. In either example, and at all aerodromes that fall between these extremes, the 'last line of defence' against runway incursion will always be the pilot.

Any pilot may remember being taught to cross the road safely, a process that might have been summarised as *"Stop, Look, Listen"*. The same idea can be applied to preventing runway incursion, in principle:

Stop If you are unsure of your position in relation to a runway, unsure of whether you can enter or cross a runway, or unsure if a runway may already be occupied, the simplest course of action is to stop.

Look Before entering or crossing a runway, regardless of any ATC clearance, always look out both along the runway itself and along the final approach path to satisfy yourself that it is safe to proceed.

Listen Listen out not just for ATC instructions or information (if applicable), but also for transmissions from other aircraft, to form a mental picture of where other aircraft or vehicles are and what they are doing. Nevertheless, do remember that aircraft or vehicles may be operating non-radio (or on a different radio frequency) at many airfields.

Figure AL3.16
A runway incursion which caused the landing aircraft to 'go-around'.

Figure AL3.17
An accident as a result of a runway incursion (an aircraft attempted to take-off as another aircraft was landing, neither saw the other), fortunately all occupants escaped without injury. The accident investigation determined that the probable cause was, *"The departing pilot's inadequate visual lookout. Contributing to the accident were the trees/visual obstructions along the runway's approach path."*

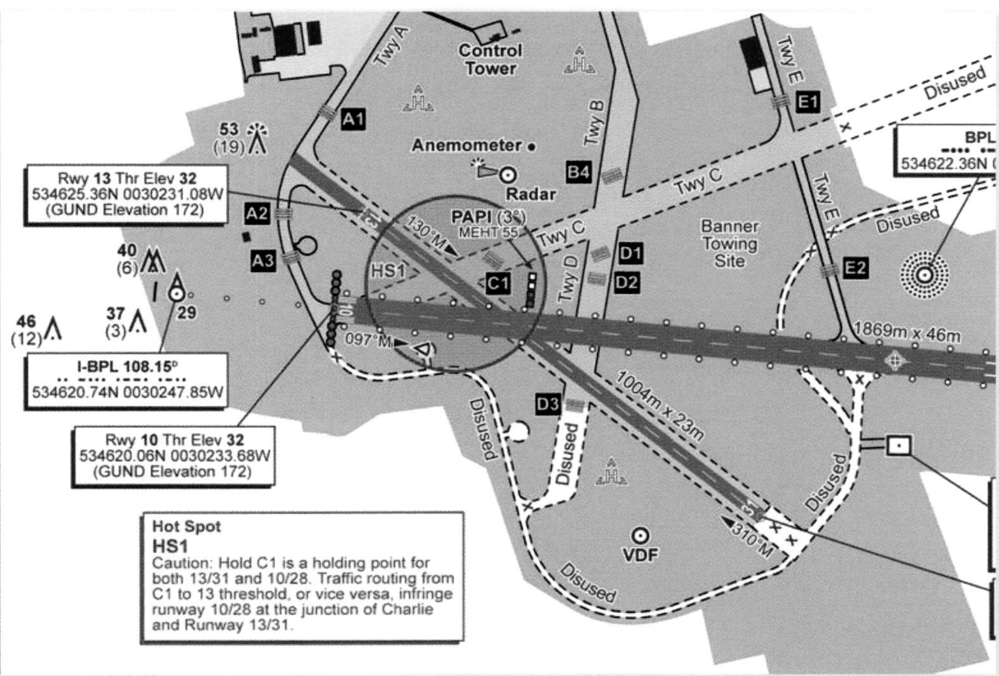

Figure AL3.18
On this official airfield chart an incursion 'Hot Spot' is marked with explanatory note.

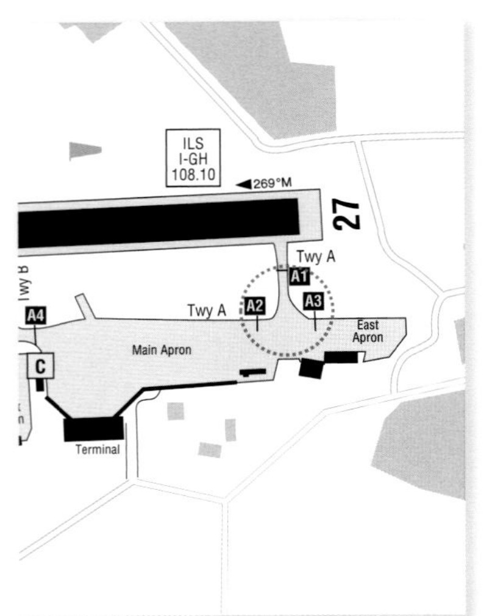

Figure AL3.19
Another incursion Hot Spot as depicted on a commercial airfield guide.

To help navigation around an airfield (especially one you are not familiar with) it is good practice to have an aerodrome chart available to monitor your position. As well as portraying runways, taxiways, holding points etc. an aerodrome chart should depict any incursion 'hot spots' at an airfield. A 'hot spot' is a zone or area on the airfield in which incursions have taken place, or in which there is an increased risk of incursion. Clearly, extra caution is needed when taxiing in a 'hot spot' location.

When taxiing at an airfield a pilot should always be aware of the risk of runway incursion, factors that increase the risk of runway incursion include:

- Operating at an unfamiliar airfield;
- Airfields with complicated taxiing procedures and/or multiple runways and taxiways;
- Poor visibility conditions, low sun or night-time;
- Pilots not conforming to existing or recommended traffic patterns – for example using a different runway or flying a different circuit pattern to established circuit traffic;
- Operations in 'hot spots'.

Flight safety is very often a matter of following established procedures unless there is a very good reason not to. Many aviation rules and procedures have been created as a consequence of incidents and accidents – in other words, mistakes learnt the hard way. To avoid repeating these mistakes, and to integrate safely with other traffic, following the established rules and procedures is most often the 'golden rule' in flight safety. In relation to preventing runway incursions, the rules and procedures particularly relevant from those already described are:

- The Pilot In Command (PIC) is ultimately responsible for the safety of the aircraft;
- An aircraft on the ground must give way to aircraft landing or in the final stages of an approach to land;
- Aircraft on the ground must give way to aircraft taking off or about to take-off;
- Aircraft at a controlled aerodrome must stop and hold at all runway-holding positions, until clearance to enter or cross the runway has been issued by ATC;
- Aircraft must stop and hold at all lit stop bars and may only proceed further in accordance with an ATC clearance, when the lights are switched off;
- And remember: Stop, Look, Listen.

Other ground signals

In addition to the markings and signals already described, there are other indicators which may be used at airfields.

Air traffic services reporting office
A yellow square board framing a black letter 'C' indicates the location of the 'air traffic services reporting office'. This is the point to which visiting pilots are expected to report after landing (for example to 'book in').

Take-off direction
A two digit number, displayed on or near the control tower indicates the take-off direction in use (in tens of degrees).

Figure AL3.20
a Air traffic services reporting office
b Take-off direction

Figure AL3.21
A black C on a yellow board indicates the air traffic services reporting office, the place for visiting pilots to report to.

There may be other signals, visible to an aircraft in flight, used to give information about the aerodrome surface, hazards, operations or special instructions. These signals are usually displayed in a 'signal area' – an area on an aerodrome used for the display of ground signals. Not all aerodromes are required to display such signals and with the passage of time, their use is becoming less common. Nevertheless, an aircraft observing one or more of these the signals must take such action as may be required by the signal.

Figure AL3.22
Where they exist, ground signals are usually displayed within a signal square.

Figure AL3.23
Signs in the signal area

Landing Prohibited	a red square panel with yellow diagonals indicates that landings are prohibited and that the prohibition is liable to be prolonged.
Special Precautions Required	a red square panel with one yellow diagonal indicates that owing to the bad state of the manoeuvring area, or for some other reason, special precautions must be observed when approaching to land or landing.
Use of runways and taxiways	a white dumb-bell indicates that aircraft are required to land, take-off and taxi on runways and taxiways only.
Use of runways	a white dumb-bell with a black bar across each circular portion of the dumb-bell indicates that aircraft are required to land and take-off on runways only, but other ground manoeuvres need not be confined to runways and taxiways.
Right-hand traffic	a right-hand arrow of conspicuous colour indicates that turns are to be made to the right before landing and after take-off (eg a right-hand circuit).
Direction for landing or take-off	a horizontal white or orange landing 'T' indicates the direction to be used by aircraft for landing and take-off, which is in the direction parallel to the shaft of the 'T' towards the cross arm.
Sailplane flying in operation	a double white cross indicates that the aerodrome is being used by sailplanes (gliders) and that sailplane flights are being performed.

Figure AL3.24
a Landing Prohibited
b Special Precautions Required
c Aircraft are required to land, take-off and taxi on runways and taxiways only
d Aircraft are required to land and take-off on runways only, but other ground manoeuvres need not be confined to runways and taxiways
e Right-hand traffic
f Direction for landing or take-off
g Sailplane flying in operation

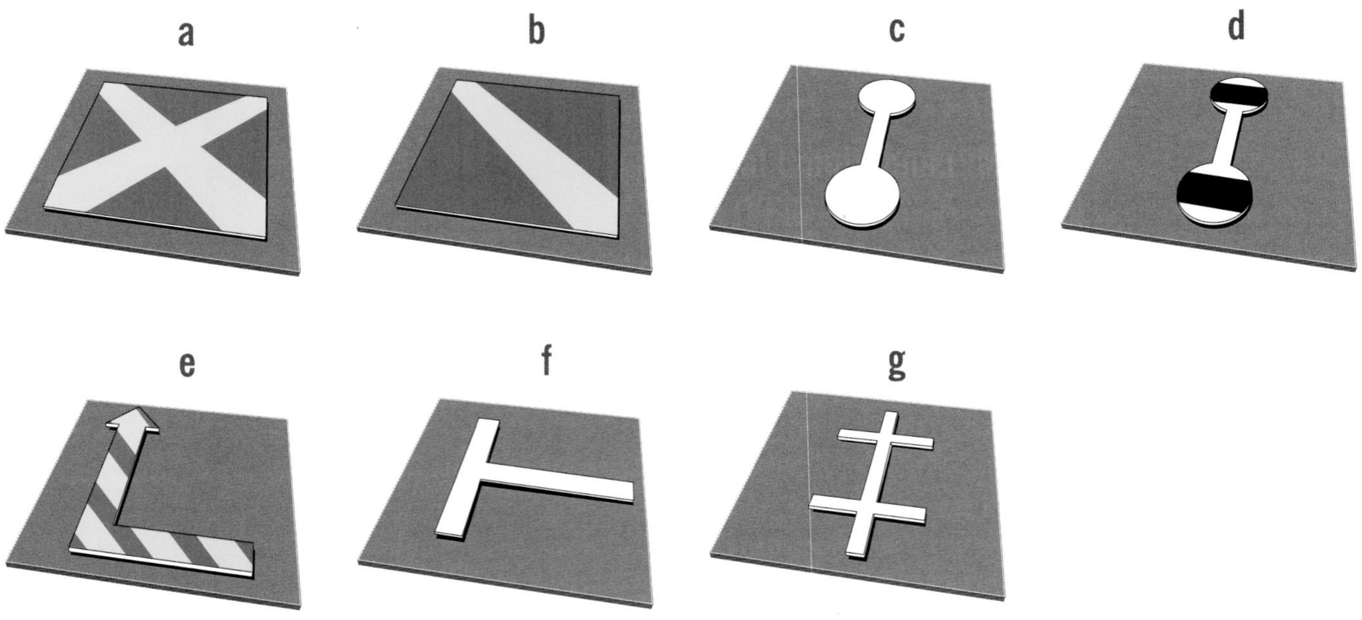

Figure AL3.25
The edge of the airfield, or areas on an airfield that are unfit for the movement of aircraft, may be signified by marker boards, flags or cones with alternating orange/white, red/white or yellow/white stripes

Figure AL3.26
Fixed obstructions on an airfield may be painted with red and white bands or a 'chequer-board' pattern to make them more conspicuous.

The edge of the airfield, or areas that are unfit for the movement of aircraft, may be signified by markings consisting of marker boards, flags or cones with alternating orange/white, red/white or yellow/white stripes.

Fixed obstructions on, or close to, an airfield may be painted with red and white bands or a 'chequer-board' pattern to make them visible at significant distances and in poor visibility.

Figure AL3.27
A windsock.

Overhead wires and cables close to an airfield may be very difficult to spot. For this reason, they may be made more noticeable by placing coloured spheres along the wires or cables at regular intervals.

Another ground signal, as old as flying itself and still found at any flying site, from the biggest international airport to smallest airstrip, is the humble windsock (sometimes called the 'wind direction indicator'). The 'sleeve' of the windsock will be brightly coloured – often dayglow orange or yellow. The direction in which the sleeve is 'flying' is the surface wind direction, the closer to horizontal the sleeve is, the stronger the wind. Although there is no internationally agreed standard for the wind speed at which the windsock sleeve will become horizontal, as a general rule at a major airport the windsock becomes horizontal at around 25-30 knots.

The windsock is a much underestimated aid to the pilot. In addition to determining the take-off and landing direction for even the largest aircraft, observation of the windsock before take-off and landing will give the pilot valuable information about the behaviour of the surface wind. At some airfields, there may be a significant variation in wind direction and velocity at different locations. A windsock close to the runway in use may give more relevant information on the wind conditions there than the wind being reported on the radio from a place that could be more than a mile away.

Marshalling signals

Whilst taxiing or parking, the pilot may receive **marshalling** signals. These signals are provided for the guidance of the pilot and, according to the Rules of the Air, a pilot can disregard marshalling signals if *"...absolutely necessary in the interests of safety."* As always, the over-riding principle is that the pilot in command (PIC) has the ultimate responsibility for the safety of the aircraft and passengers, and in matters of safety the pilot in command has the final say.

The person providing the marshalling signals is responsible for giving the signals in a *"...clear and precise manner."* In practice, the pilot has no obvious way of knowing if someone giving marshalling signals has had full marshalling training, or not. Incidentally, pilots themselves are often very poor at giving clear marshalling signals to other pilots! This only emphasises the point that the pilot in command must make a judgement about the validity of any marshalling signals being given, and the safety of following the implied instruction or advice.

Figure AL3.28
Marshalling signals

Wingwalker/guide (This signal by a person positioned at the aircraft wing tip, to the pilot or marshaller/push-back operator, indicates that aircraft movement on or off a parking position would be unobstructed).

Identify gate (This indicates the parking area, stand or gate the aircraft is being marshalled to).

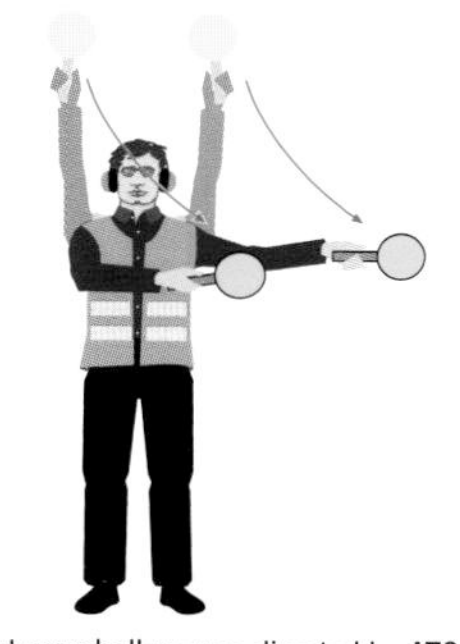

Proceed to next marshaller or as directed by ATC

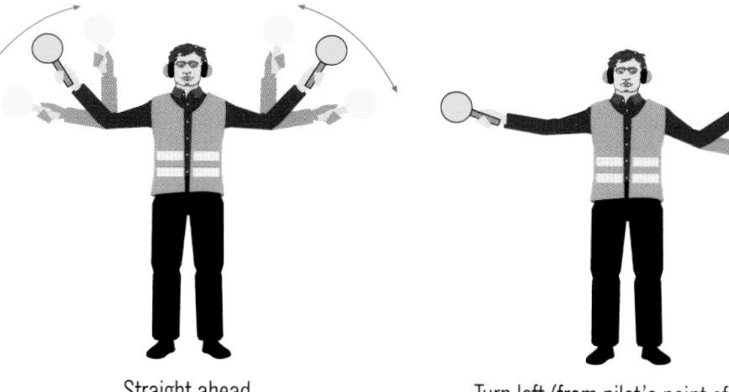

Straight ahead

Turn left (from pilot's point of view)

Turn right (from pilot's point of view)

Slow down

Normal stop

Emergency stop
Hold position/stand by
Set brakes
Release brakes
Chocks inserted
Chocks removed
Start engine(s)
Cut engines
Slow down engine(s) on indicated side
Move back
Turns while backing (for tail to starboard/right)
Turns while backing (for tail to port/ left)
Affirmative/all clear
Dispatch aircraft

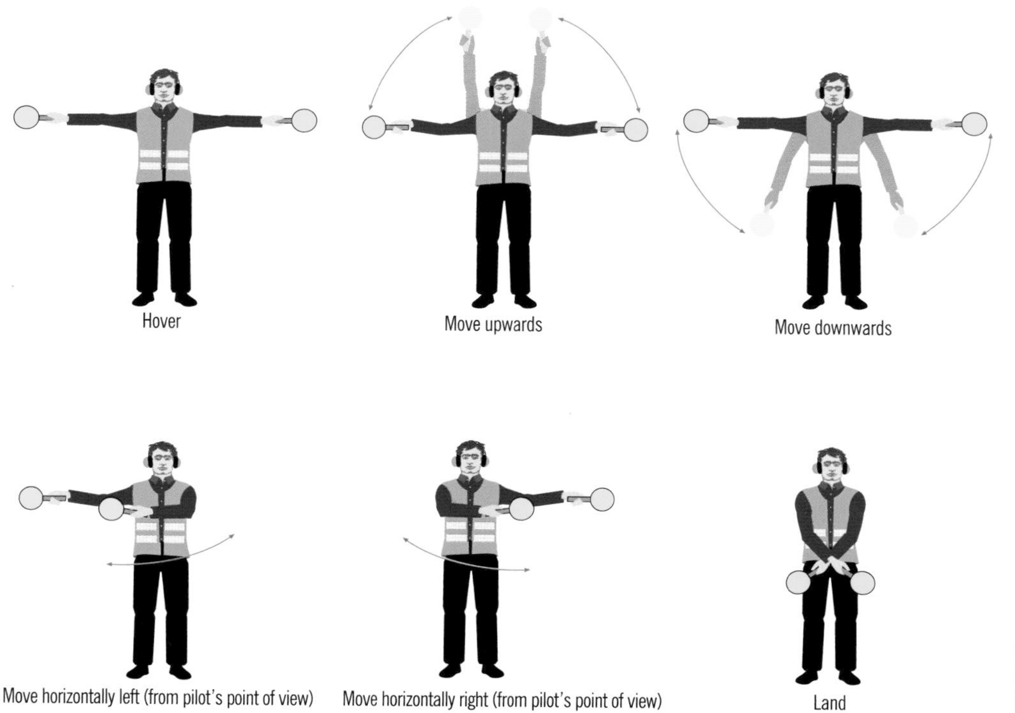

Figure AL3.29
The following signals may be given to hovering helicopters:

AL3.30
In an emergency, the following signals may also be given:

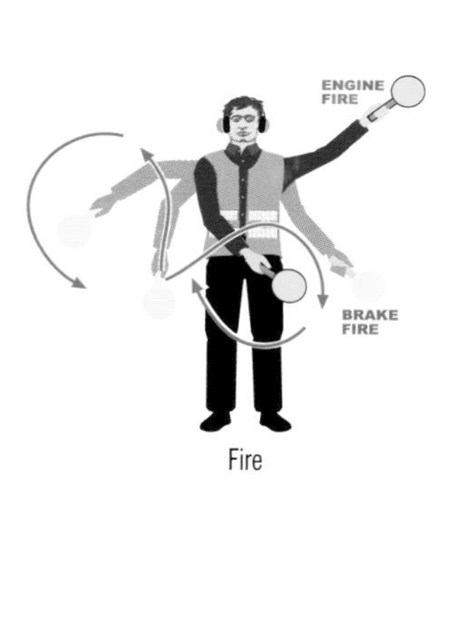

Fire

Recommend stop

Recommend evacuation

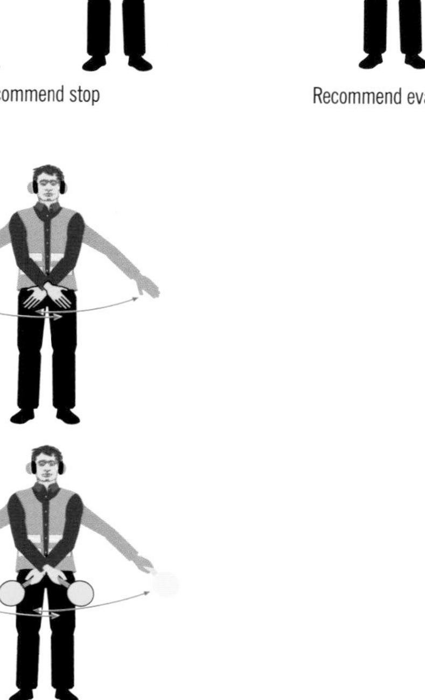
Emergency contained

Figure AL3.31
A pilot may also give the following signals to a marshaller or other ground personnel:

Light signals

Although in practice the use of light signals is a rarity, the pilot is required to know the basic light signals that may be directed towards an aircraft, and the correct acknowledgment:

Light Signal	To an aircraft in flight	To an aircraft on the ground
Steady green	Cleared to land	Cleared for take-off
Steady red	Give way to other aircraft and continue circling	Stop
Series of green flashes	Return for landing (*)	Cleared to taxi
Series of red flashes	Aerodrome unsafe, do not land	Taxi clear of landing area in use
Series of white flashes	Land at this aerodrome and proceed to apron (*)	Return to starting point on the aerodrome

(*) Clearances to land and to taxi will be given in due course.

Figure AL3.32
The meaning of light signals to an aircraft on the ground or in flight.

A red pyrotechnic (such as a flare or firework-style signal) means that, regardless of any previous instruction, do not land for the time-being.

Figure AL3.33
A summary of ground to air visual signals:
a. Give way and continue circling
b. Do not land here
c. You may land
d. Return to this airfield
e. Land at this airfield

A light signal can be acknowledged in the following ways:

Aircraft in flight by day	**Aircraft in flight at night**
By rocking the aircraft's wings, except for the base and final legs of the approach	By flashing the aircraft's landing lights on and off twice or, if not so equipped, by switching its navigation lights on and off twice.
Aircraft on ground by day	**Aircraft on ground at night**
By moving the aircraft's ailerons or rudder	By flashing the aircraft's landing lights on and off twice or, if not so equipped, by switching its navigation lights on and off twice.

Figure AL3.34
'Acknowledgement' signals from an aircraft to indicate that a light signal has been received and understood.

Progress Check

19. What is the meaning of this taxiway sign?

20. What is the meaning of this marking painted on a taxiway?

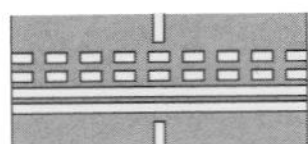

21. What is the meaning of this sign?

22. What is the meaning of this marking painted on a runway or taxiway?

23. What is the full meaningof this runway threshold marking?

24. What does this PAPI indication mean?

25. What is the meaning of this marking on an airfield chart?

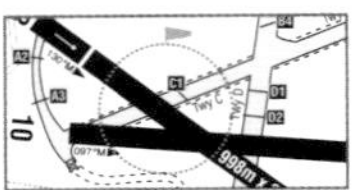

26. What is the meaning of this signal on the side of an airfield building?

27. What is the meaning of this ground signal?

28. What is designated by this marker board?

29. What is the meaning of this marshalling signal?

30. What is the meaning of this marshalling signal?

31. What is the meaning of this marshalling signal to a helicopter?

32. What is the meaning of this emergency marshalling signal?

33. How can a pilot indicate that he or she is ready to start the engine(s)?
34. What is the meaning of the following light signal to an aircraft in flight?

STEADY RED

These questions are intended to test knowledge and reinforce some of the key learning points from this section. In answering these questions, a 'pass rate' of around 80% should be the target.

Model answers are found at page 144

AL4 Visual Meteorological Conditions (VMC) and Visual Flight Rules (VFR)

Visual Meteorological Conditions (VMC) minima

Visual Flight Rules (VFR)

Minimum Heights

Visual Meteorological Conditions (VMC) and Visual Flight Rules (VFR)

Visual Meteorological Conditions (VMC) minima

In essence, an aircraft can be controlled by the pilot either by reference to the view outside or, if this is not possible, by sole reference to the flight instruments. The business of controlling, navigating and avoiding other aircraft by external reference involves the **Visual Flight Rules** – known as '**VFR**'. In principle, flying VFR means being able to control the aircraft, navigate it and avoid collisions (either with other aircraft or with the ground or obstructions) all by looking out of the windows. It follows that flying under VFR is only possible if the weather conditions, such as cloud base and visibility, are good enough to give the pilot adequate external visual references. It is an essential requirement for VFR flight that the weather conditions at any time during the flight meet criteria known as **Visual Meteorological Conditions** (**VMC**).

Put simply, to fly under VFR the aircraft must be in VMC.

Figure AL4.1
Visual Meteorological Conditions (VMC) minima are based primarily on flight visibility and distance from cloud.
To fly VFR, the aircraft must be in VMC.

The Standardised European Rules of the Air (SERA) define Visual Meteorological Conditions (VMC) as *"...meteorological conditions expressed in terms of visibility, distance from cloud, and cloud ceiling, equal to or better than specified minima."* What constitutes 'VMC' can vary with a number of factors, including how high the aircraft is flying and what type of airspace the aircraft is flying in. VMC does not vary with the size of the aircraft nor the type of licence held by the PIC.

Some of what follows can seem quite complex at first, but is easier to understand if approached in stages.

To start, it is necessary to know that airspace is divided into seven 'classifications' or 'classes'.

- Airspace classified as class A, B, C, D or E is a type of 'controlled 'airspace.
- Airspace classified as class F or G is a type of 'uncontrolled' airspace.

Airspace classifications are explained in more detail in a later section.

The first criteria for determining VMC minima is the aircraft 'altitude', that is, its vertical distance 'above mean sea level' – (amsl).

At and above 10,000ft amsl (or alternatively 'Flight Level' 100, this term is explained in a later section), and in all classes of airspace, VMC minima are:

- Flight visibility at least 8 kilometres,
- A distance of at least 1500 meters horizontally and 1000ft vertically from cloud.

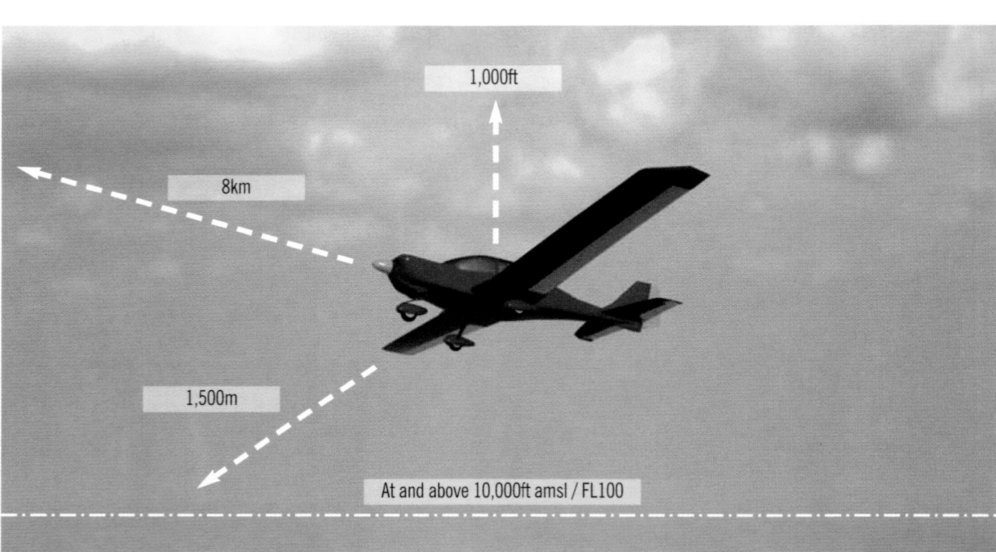

Figure AL4.2
At and above 10,000ft amsl / FL100, VMC minima are:
flight visibility at least 8 kilometres,
at least 1500 meters horizontally and 1000ft vertically clear of cloud.

The use of different units for vertical and horizontal distances is a reflection of ICAO standards which recommend, in general, that 'feet' are used for vertical distances and metres/kilometres for horizontal distances. These recommendations are not applied universally.

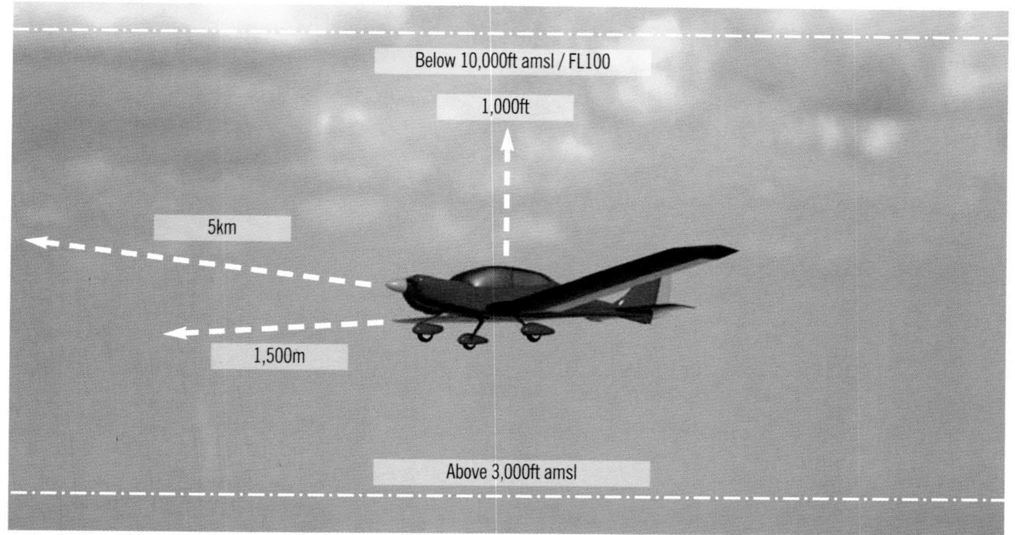

Figure AL4.3
Below 10,000ft amsl / FL 100 and above 3000ft amsl (or 1000ft above terrain, whichever is higher), VMC minima are:
flight visibility at least 5 kilometres,
at least 1500 meters horizontally and 1000ft vertically clear of cloud.

Below 10,000ft amsl (or alternatively 'Flight Level' 100), and above 3000ft amsl (or 1000ft above terrain, whichever is higher), in all classes of airspace, VMC minima are:

- Flight visibility at least 5 kilometres,
- A distance of at least 1500 meters horizontally and 1000ft vertically from cloud.

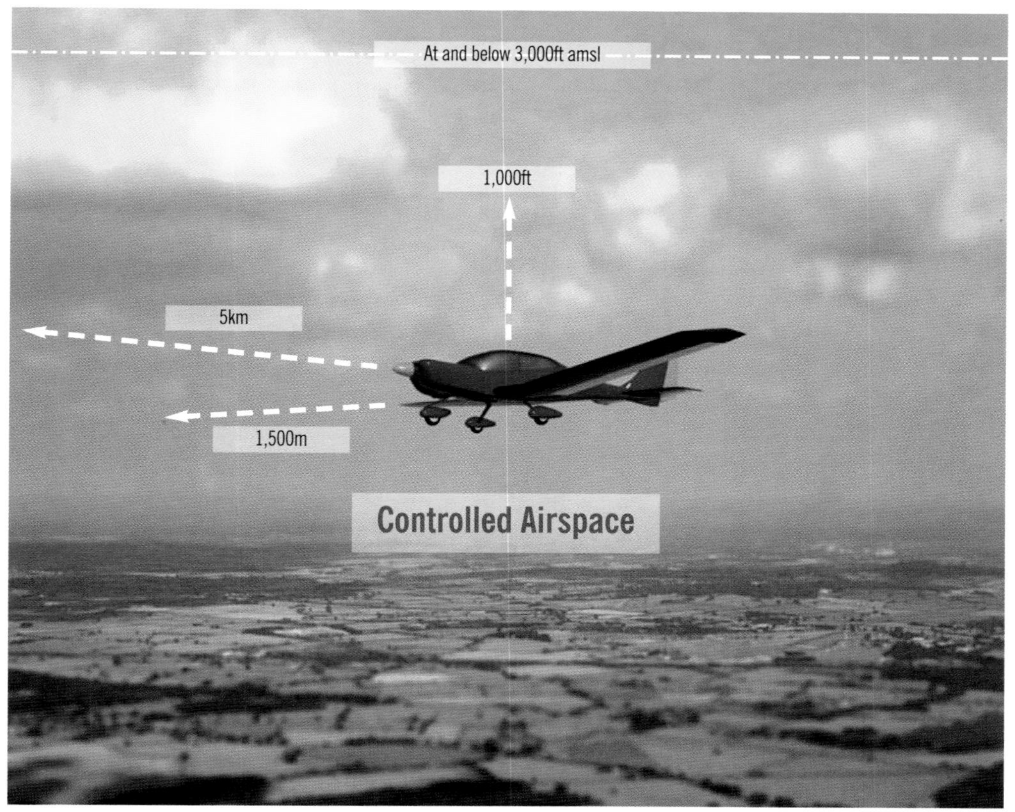

Figure AL4.4
In controlled airspace, at and below 3000ft amsl (or 1000ft above terrain, whichever is higher), VMC minima are:
flight visibility at least 5 kilometres,
at least 1500 meters horizontally and 1000ft vertically clear of cloud

At and below 3000ft amsl, or 1000ft above terrain (whichever is higher), in controlled airspace (Class A, B, C D or E) VMC minima are:

- Flight visibility at least 5 kilometres,
- A distance of at least 1500 meters horizontally and 1000ft vertically from cloud.

Figure AL4.5
In uncontrolled airspace at and below 3000ft amsl (or 1000ft above terrain, whichever is higher), VMC minima are:
flight visibility at least 5 kilometres,
clear of cloud and with the surface in sight.

At and below 3000ft amsl, or 1000ft above terrain (whichever is higher), in uncontrolled airspace (Class F or G) VMC minima are:

- Flight visibility at least 5 kilometres,
- Clear of cloud and with the surface in sight

If a 'competent authority' allows, in Class F & G (uncontrolled) airspace, at and below 3000ft amsl or 1000ft above terrain (whichever is higher), VMC visibility minima can be further reduced based on aircraft speed:

- At 140 knots indicated airspeed or less, flight visibility not less than 1500 metres;
- For a helicopter, if manoeuvred at a speed that will give adequate opportunity to observe other traffic or obstacles in time to avoid collision, flight visibility not less than 800 metres.

Figure AL4.6
In uncontrolled airspace at and below 3000ft amsl (or 1000ft above terrain, whichever is higher), the competent authority may allow VMC visibility minima to be reduced for an aeroplane flying at 140 knots indicated airspeed or less, to:
flight visibility not less than 1500 metres,
clear of cloud and with the surface in sight.

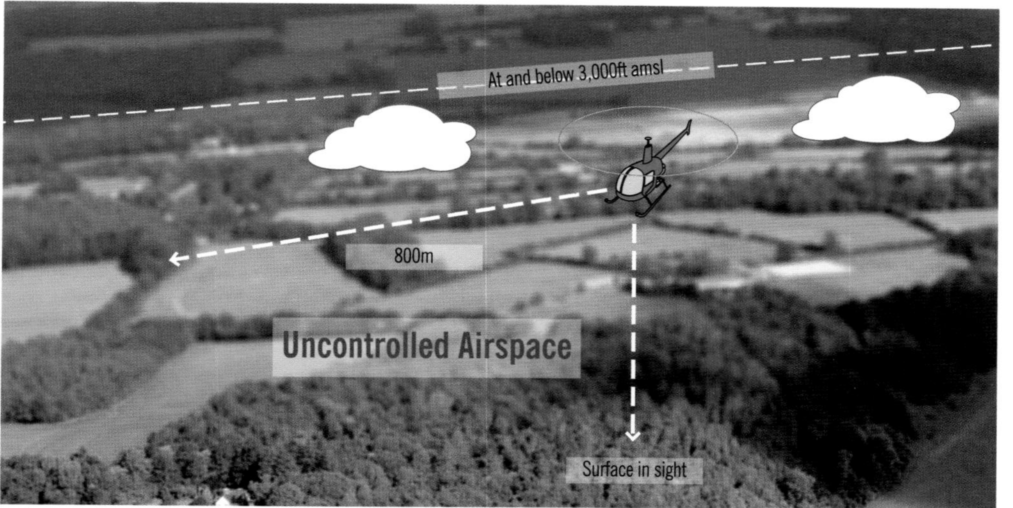

Figure AL4.7
In uncontrolled airspace at and below 3000ft amsl (or 1000ft above terrain, whichever is higher), the competent authority may allow VMC visibility minima to be reduced for a helicopter, if manoeuvred at a speed that will give adequate opportunity to observe other traffic or obstacles in time to avoid collision, to:
flight visibility not less than 800 metres,
clear of cloud and with the surface in sight.

Flight visibility means the visibility forward from the cockpit of an aircraft in flight. It is the Pilot In Command who is responsible for assessing in-flight conditions to decide if they are VMC or not.

Because VMC criteria vary with a number of different factors, principally aircraft level and class of airspace, it will probably require reading and re-reading of the above to remember the necessary numbers. A simple and practical way to help retain and remember the VMC minima is to assess the weather conditions on each flight in relation to VMC requirements. This should help in acquiring a practical appreciation of VMC and how it can vary in different situations. Nevertheless, probably the most important point about VMC, and one sometimes forgotten in practical flying, is the simple principle:

to fly under VFR, the aircraft must be in VMC.

Figure AL4.8
A summary of Visual Meteorological Conditions (VMC) minima.

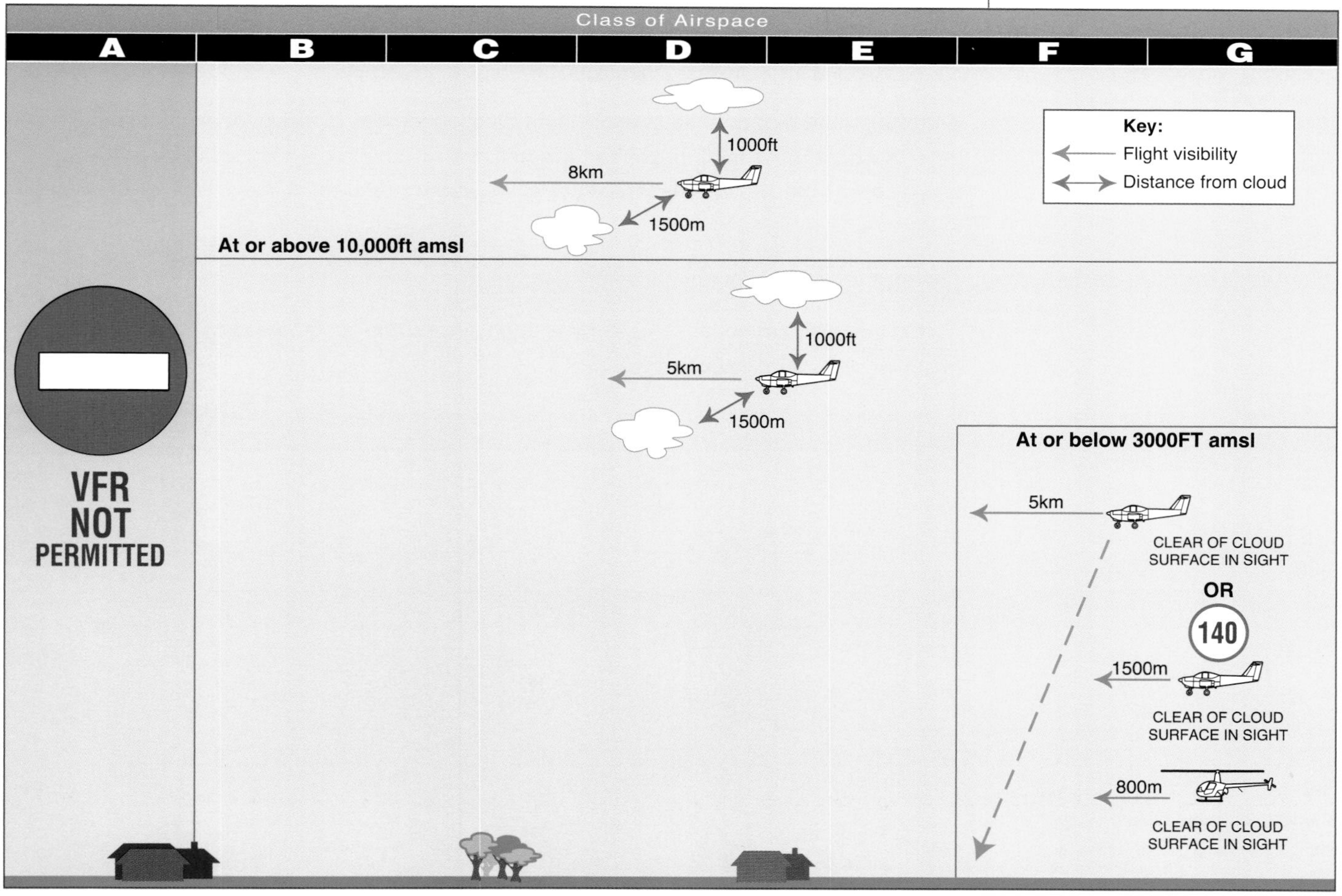

Class of Airspace
A B C D E F G

VFR NOT PERMITTED

At or above 10,000ft amsl
1000ft
8km
1500m

1000ft
5km
1500m

At or below 3000FT amsl
5km
CLEAR OF CLOUD
SURFACE IN SIGHT
OR
140
1500m
CLEAR OF CLOUD
SURFACE IN SIGHT
800m
CLEAR OF CLOUD
SURFACE IN SIGHT

Key:
Flight visibility
Distance from cloud

Visual Flight Rules (VFR)

The flight rules under which a flight is operating are fundamental to deciding many aspects of the aircraft's operation, including such matters as minimum altitudes, courses to be flown, responsibility for avoiding collisions, ATC liaison, altimeter setting procedures and many more. Rather than trying to list all these rules in one place, possibly out of context, the requirements for VFR flight will be dealt with as appropriate in the following sections. Nevertheless, in general terms it is fair to consider that the pilot in command of a VFR flight (that is, a flight conducted in accordance with the Visual Flight Rules) has a high degree of freedom in deciding where to fly, who to talk to, what levels to fly at and which pilot licences and ratings and aircraft equipment are required.

The fact that VMC minima inside controlled airspace are more restrictive than those in uncontrolled airspace can cause problems when a VFR flight wishes to operate to and from an airfield located inside controlled airspace. Controlled airspace which extends upwards from the surface (in other words, it's not possible to fly under it!) is known as a 'control zone'. Most major airports are surrounded by a control zone so ATC can establish what Air Traffic Controllers sometimes call a 'known traffic environment'.

In addition to the VMC minima for controlled airspace already described, VFR flights must not take-off or land at an aerodrome within a control zone, nor enter the aerodrome's traffic zone (described later), nor enter the aerodrome's traffic circuit, when the reported meteorological conditions at that aerodrome are below the following minima:

- Cloud ceiling less than 1,500ft; or
- Ground visibility less than 5km.

In contrast to the normal assessment of in-flight conditions by the pilot in command, determining if these minima are met inside a control zone is the responsibility of ATC, usually based on the official meteorological observations at the airfield. Each of the criteria has a specific definition:

Cloud ceiling means the height above the surface of the base of the lowest layer of cloud (if below 20,000ft), covering more than half the sky.

Ground visibility means the visibility at an aerodrome, as reported by an accredited observer or by automatic systems.

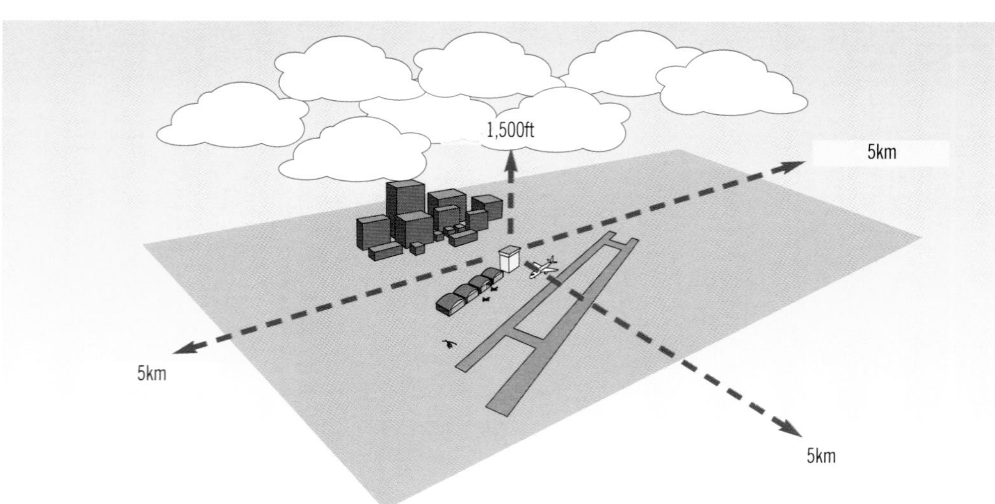

Figure AL4.9
When taking off, landing and operating close to an airport within a control zone, additional weather minima apply to a VFR flight.

If VMC minima cannot be met, the aircraft is now in conditions known as **Instrument Meteorlogical Conditions** (**IMC**). In IMC, VFR flight is not permitted and the aircraft must be operated in accordance with **Instrument Flight Rules** (**IFR**). IFR flight involves many more rules and regulations than VFR flight, including in particular additional pilot qualifications, and is outside the scope of this book. Nevertheless, there is one specific circumstance when a flight can operate in conditions that are less than VMC, without having to comply with IFR.

To allow a flight to operate within a control zone when weather conditions do not meet VMC minima, there is a concept known as 'Special VFR'. A **Special VFR flight** is a VFR flight cleared by ATC to operate within a control zone in meteorological conditions below VMC minima. In order to accept a Special VFR clearance within a control zone, the pilot in command must ensure that the following criteria are met:

- Clear of cloud and with the surface in sight;
- Flight visibility not less than 1500m (for helicopters, not less than 800m);
- Indicated air speed of 140kts or less to give adequate opportunity to observe other traffic and any obstacles in time to avoid a collision.

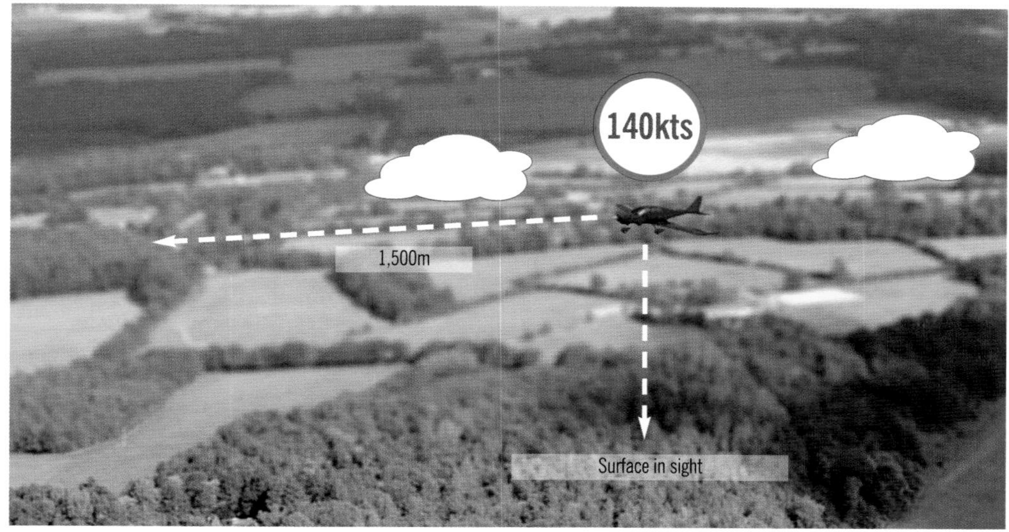

Figure AL4.10
Minimum conditions for a Special VFR flight in an aeroplane.

Figure AL4.11
Minimum conditions for a Special VFR flight in a helicopter.

Additionally, ATC may only issue a Special VFR clearance:

- During day only (unless otherwise permitted by the competent authority);
- When the ground visibility is not less than 1500m (for helicopters, not less than 800m);
- When the cloud ceiling is not less than 600ft.

Even when operating as a VFR flight, there are certain situations in which it is mandatory to establish and maintain radio contact an ATC unit. Those circumstances are:

Figure AL4.12
Situations in which a VFR flight must establish and maintain radio contact with an ATC unit.

When operating within Class B, C or D airspace In principle, it is necessary to contact ATC for permission to enter Class B, C or D airspace as a VFR flight, and then maintain contact with the ATC unit. A VFR flight is also expected to comply with ATC instructions unless the pilot specifically states otherwise. VFR flight is not permitted within Class A airspace.
When operating at, or in the traffic pattern at, a 'controlled aerodrome' At a controlled aerodrome (that is, an aerodrome at which an ATC service is provided), ATC permission is also required before taxiing on the manoeuvring area, the pilot in command is normally required to comply with ATC instructions. ATC permission is also required to enter the traffic pattern at a controlled aerodrome.
When operating as a Special VFR flight

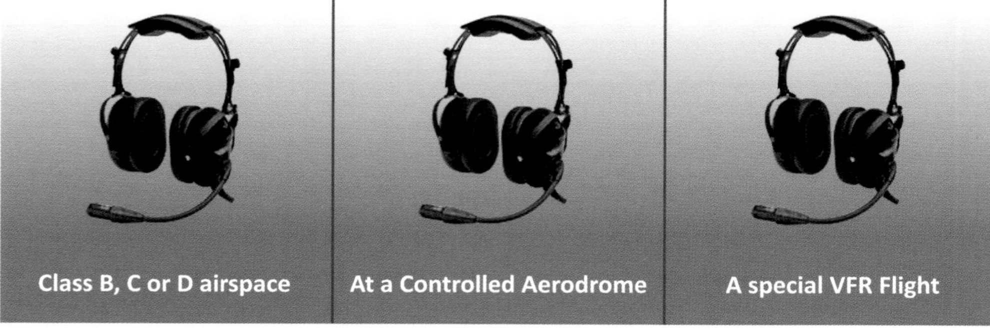

Figure AL4.13
Three specific circumstances where a VFR flight is required to establish and maintain radio contact with an ATC unit.

In the event that ATC offer the pilot a clearance which is not satisfactory, or is unsafe, or which the pilot cannot comply with, the pilot-in-command must inform ATC that the clearance is not acceptable. ATC will then issue an amended clearance if practicable. An example of this situation would an ATC height or heading instruction which would take a VFR flight into cloud. It is the pilot's responsibility to inform ATC that he or she cannot comply with the clearance.

Magnetic Track			
000° – 179°		180° – 359°	
Flight Level	**Altitude**	**Flight Level**	**Altitude**
FL035	3,500ft	FL045	4,500ft
FL055	5,500ft	FL065	6,500ft
FL075	7,500ft	FL085	8,500ft
FL095	9,500ft	FL105	10,500ft
FL115	11,500ft	FL125	12,500ft
FL135	13,500ft	FL145	14,500ft
FL155	15,500ft	FL165	16,500ft
FL175	17,500ft	FL185	18,500ft
FL195	19,500ft	FL205	20,500ft
FL215	21,500ft	FL225	22,500ft
FL235	23,500ft	FL245	24,500ft
FL255	25,500ft	FL265	26,500ft
FL275	27,500ft	FL285	28,500ft

Figure AL4.14
The cruising levels for a VFR flight, based on magnetic track.

When a VFR flight is in level cruising flight above 3000ft amsl (or a higher level if specified by the 'Competent Authority'), the cruising level should be chosen in accordance with the table above. The cruising levels for a VFR flight are based on **magnetic track**, which is the aircraft's path over the surface, referenced to magnetic north.

A level above the 3000ft amsl datum may be dictated by a state's 'competent authority', and either the competent authority or air traffic control may indicate a different cruising level system to that above.

As a reminder, if conditions are below VMC minima, they are IMC and a flight not operating in accordance with VFR (or Special VFR) must be operated in accordance with IFR. An IFR flight is subject to more strict rules and procedures than a VFR flight including additional rules for pilot licencing, aircraft equipment, ATC liaison, minimum heights etc.

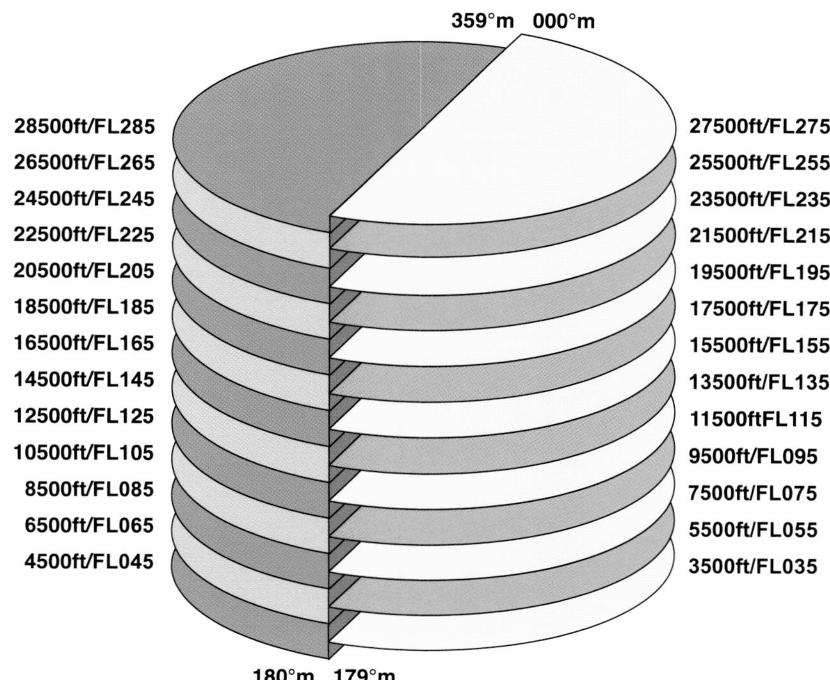

Figure AL4.15
Cruising levels for a VFR flight.

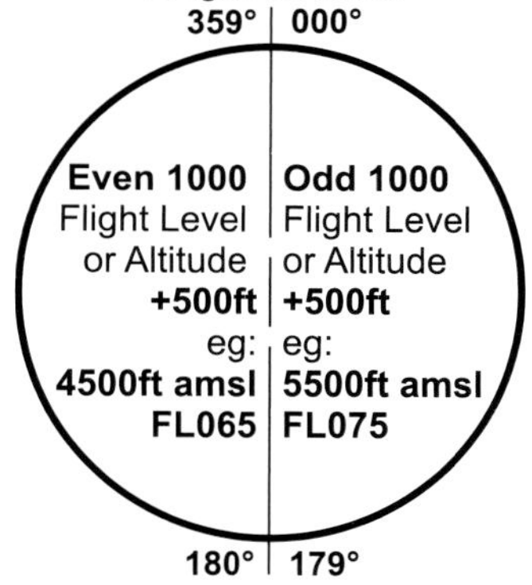

Minimum Heights

The principle minimum height rule is that, except when taking off and landing, an aircraft must not fly over the 'congested area' of a city, town or settlement, nor over an open-air assembly of people, unless it is high enough so that in an emergency it can make a landing without 'undue hazard' to persons and property on the surface. In practice this means that a single-engine aircraft must fly high enough over a congested area or open-air assembly that if the engine should fail, it could glide clear of the congested area or open-air assembly to make a safe landing.

For a VFR flight, the rules of the air set out an absolute minimum height for flying over a congested area, or open air assembly, of not less than 1000ft above the highest obstacle within a 600 metre radius of the aircraft. If it is necessary to fly higher than 1000ft above the highest obstacle in order to clear the area in the event of an emergency then pilot must do so, unless taking-off or landing.

Figure AL4.16
A congested area.

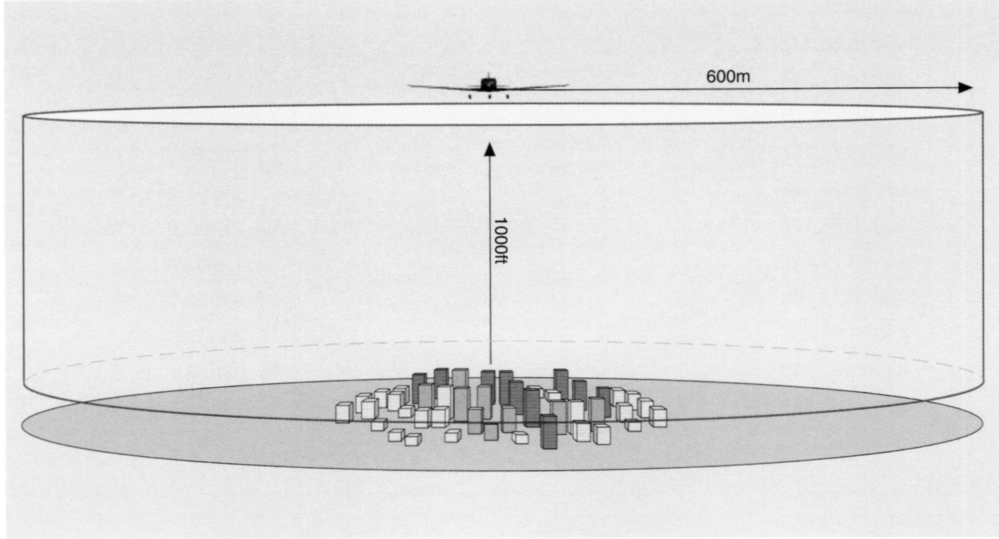

Figure AL4.17
The minimum height for flying over a congested area or open air assembly is 1000ft above the highest obstacle within a 600 metre radius, or higher if required to clear the area in the event of an emergency if higher.

Figure AL4.18
A VFR flight must not fly lower than 500ft above the surface, nor less than 500ft above the highest obstacle within 150 metres (500ft) of the aircraft.

Away from congested areas and open-air assemblies, a VFR flight must not fly lower than 500ft above the surface, nor less than 500ft above the highest obstacle within 150 metres (500ft) of the aircraft, unless taking off or landing.

Progress Check

35. What are the VMC minima below 10,000ft amsl but above 3000ft amsl?
36. What is the definition of 'Flight Visibility'?
37. What additional minima apply to a VFR flight taking off or landing at an aerodrome within a control zone?
38. What is the minimum flight visibility for an aeroplane on a Special VFR flight?
39. What is the minimum flight visibility for a helicopter on a Special VFR flight?
40. In what classes of airspace is it mandatory for a VFR flight to establish and maintain radio communications?
41. What action should a pilot take if offered an ATC clearance which is not suitable?
42. If an aircraft is in cruising level flight on a magnetic track of 135°, what level should be chosen for a VFR flight?
43. What is the minimum height for flight over a 'congested area' or open air assembly of people (except when taking off or landing)?
44. What is the minimum height for flight (except over a 'congested area') when not taking off or landing)?

These questions are intended to test knowledge and reinforce some of the key learning points from this section. In answering these questions, a 'pass rate' of around 80% should be the target.

Model answers are found at page 145

Intentionally Left Blank

AL5 Airspace Classifications

Classification of Airspace

Controlled and Notified Airspace

Uncontrolled Airspace

Radio Mandatory Zones (RMZ)

Transponder Mandatory Zones (TMZ)

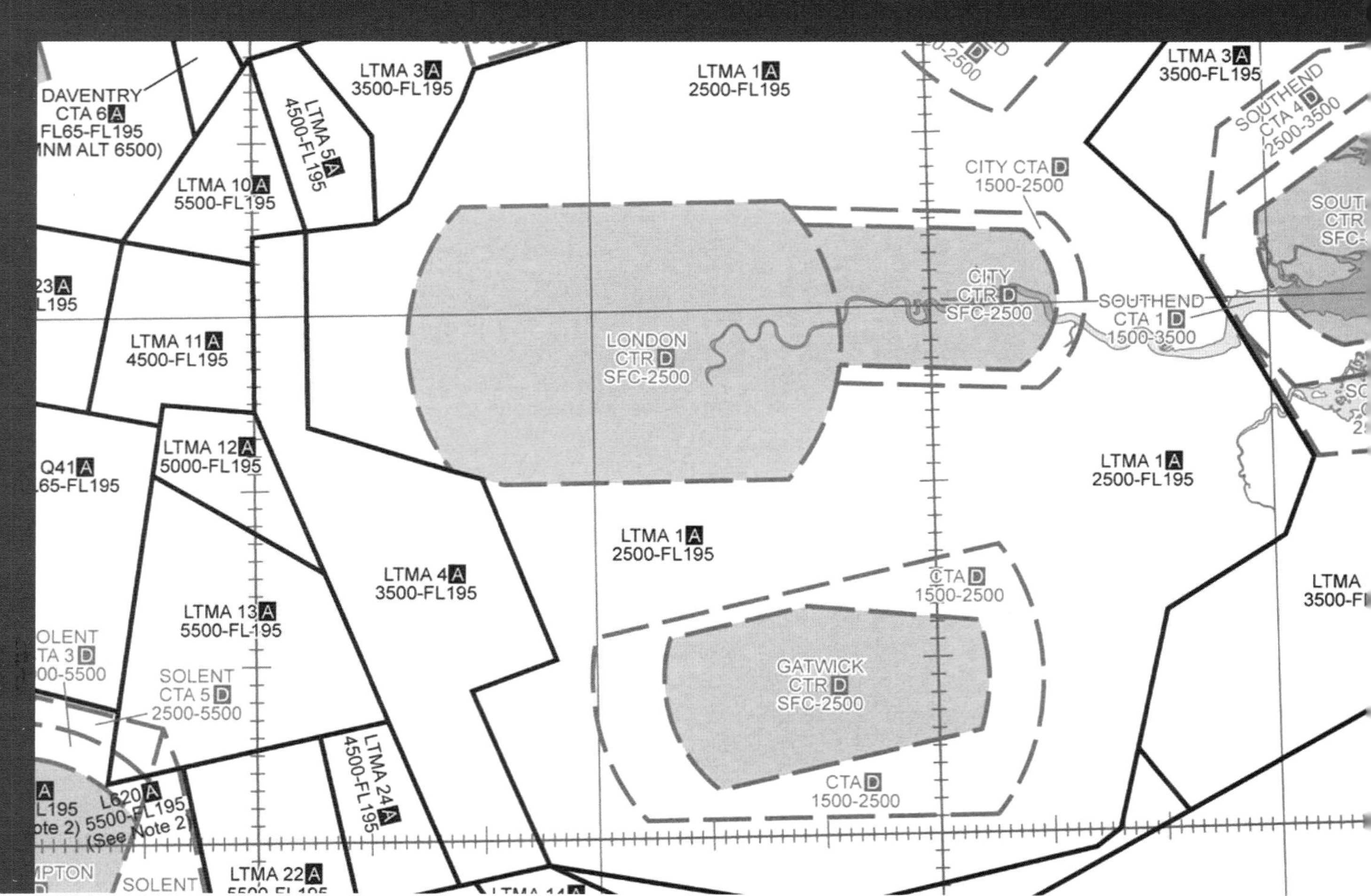

AL5 Airspace Classifications

Classification of Airspace

All airspace is divided into one of seven 'classes', from A to G, with different characteristics in terms of entry requirements, VMC minima, Air Traffic Services and, in some cases, minimum pilot ratings and aircraft equipment specifications.

Aeronautical charts designed for VFR flight will show airspace boundaries and indicate the class of airspace. As a general rule, if no airspace class is noted on the chart, it can be considered that the area is Class G airspace – the least restrictive class of uncontrolled airspace.

The designation of an area of airspace is usually based on the type of flights it is handling. Airspace used predominantly for en-route IFR flights (eg airliners and other commercial flights) tends to be the more restrictive classes of controlled airspace (such as Class A, B & C) with strict entry requirements, providing a high degree of air traffic service to ensure separation between aircraft and maintain a smooth flow of traffic. Airspace which is available to all users, but within which air traffic services may be limited or not available at all, and separation from other traffic is primarily the pilot's responsibility, will most often be Class G airspace – the most 'open' and unrestricted class of airspace.

It is quite normal for a specific location to have more than one airspace classification, depending on level and, occasionally, time of day. Thus one location may have, for example, Class G airspace from the surface to 3,500ft; Class D airspace from 3,500ft to 4,500ft, and Class A airspace above 4,500ft. It should not come as a big surprise that because aircraft operate in three dimensions, so pilots need to think in three dimensions when considering airspace.

Figure AL5.1
Any particular geographic location may have several different classes of airspace above it.

Controlled and Notified Airspace

Controlled airspace means airspace within which an air traffic control service is provided in accordance with the airspace classification. In practice this means that Classes A, B, C, D & E airspace are all controlled airspace. Class A is the most restrictive type of controlled airspace, and Class E is the most accessible controlled airspace.

VFR flight is not permitted in Class A airspace, and so Class A airspace is effectively 'off-limits' to a VFR flight, but it is included here for completeness.

The following is a summary of the key characteristics of controlled airspace in relation to VFR flight:

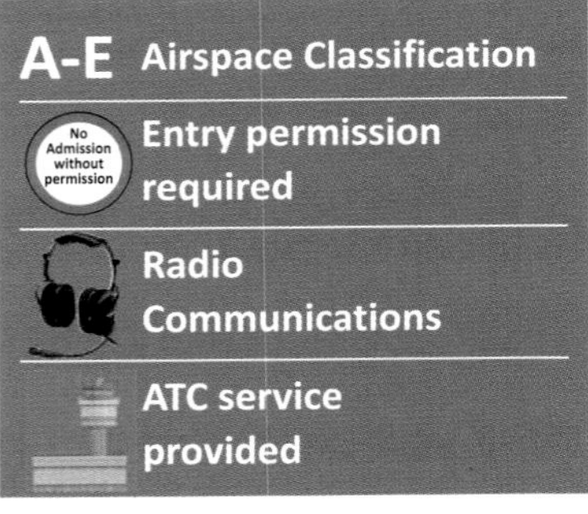

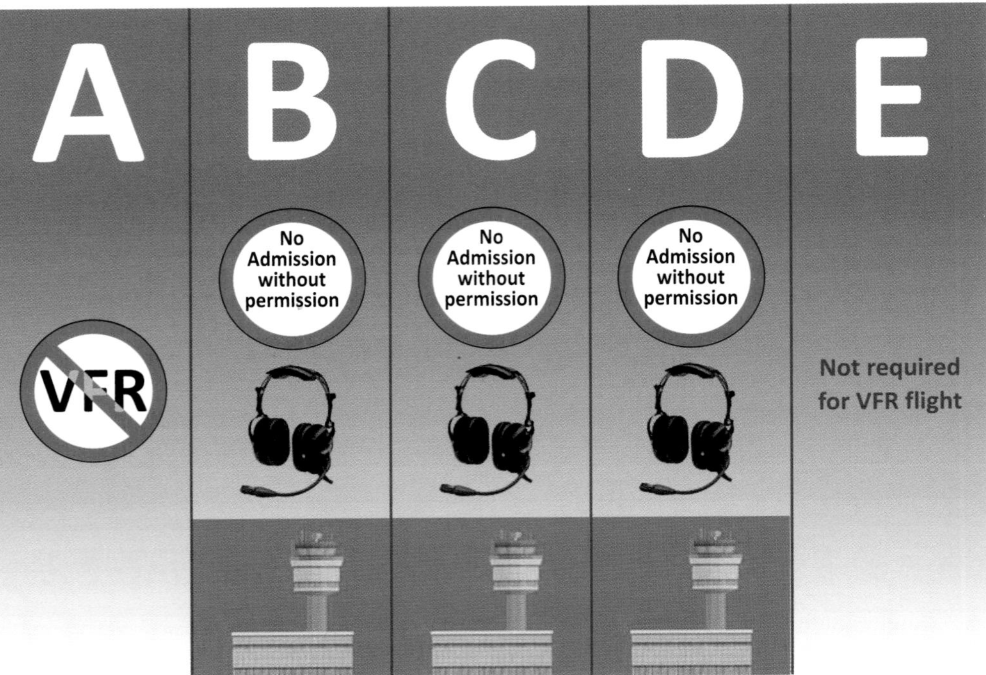

Figure AL5.2
A summary of the main requirements for a VFR flight wishing to operate in controlled airspace.

VFR Flight in Controlled Airspace	Condition	Notes
Entry subject to ATC clearance?	Yes	For all flights in Class A, B, C & D, (for IFR flights only in Class E).
Continuous air-ground voice communications?	Required	For all flights in Class A, B, C & D (and for IFR flight in Class E airspace).
Air Traffic Control Service?	Provided	To all flights in Class A, B, C & D (and to IFR flights in Class E airspace).

Figure AL5.3
A description of the principal requirements for a VFR flight operating in controlled airspace.

An **air traffic control service** means a service provided for preventing collisions between aircraft and expediting and maintaining an orderly flow of air traffic. In practice, this is achieved by flights contacting ATC and complying with ATC instructions. Except in an emergency, ATC instructions should be considered as mandatory when inside controlled airspace.

Before looking in more detail at each class of controlled airspace, there are a couple of definitions which are useful to know:

Control area	Controlled airspace extending upwards from a specified level above the earth to a specified upper limit, often abbreviated to **CTA**
Control zone	Controlled airspace extending upwards from the surface of the earth to a specified upper limit, often abbreviated to **CTR**.
Flight Level	A vertical distance in thousands of feet based on a standard altimeter setting, so Flight Level 75 is a vertical distance of 7,500ft above a standard datum which is the same across the world at all times. Abbreviated to **FL**, the use of Flight Levels in explained more fully in a later section.

Figure AL5.4
Some principal definitions in relation to Controlled Airspace.

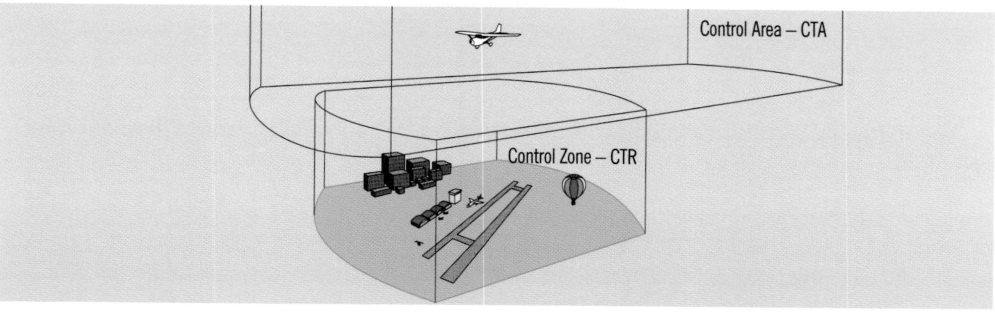

Figure AL5.5
A Control Zone (CTR) and Control Area (CTA) around and above an airport.

Each class of controlled airspace has defined characteristics.

In Class C, D and E airspace, VFR flights are subject to a general speed restriction of no more than 250 knots indicated airspeed when below 10,000ft amsl.

Class A	VFR flight is not permitted in Class A Airspace. Class A airspace is commonly used for control areas above and between major airports. Class A airspace above a major airport (or group of airports) may be a control area described as a **Terminal Manoeuvring Area (TMA)**. Class A control areas linking major airports are often in the form of a corridor known as an **airway**.
Class B	Most often used for control areas. Entry is subject to ATC clearance and continuous communications must be maintained. An air traffic control service is provided to all flights and all flights are separated from each other.
Class C	May be used for control areas and control zones. Entry is subject to ATC clearance and continuous communications must be maintained. An air traffic control service is provided to all flights. VFR flights are separated from IFR flights and receive traffic information on other VFR flights, with traffic avoidance advice available on request.
Class D	May be used for control areas and is the 'preferred' classification for control zones. Entry is subject to ATC clearance, continuous communications must be maintained. An air traffic control service is provided to all flights. VFR flights receive traffic information on all other flights, traffic avoidance advice is available on request.
Class E	May be used for control areas. VFR flights do not require ATC clearance to enter class E airspace and are not required to establish or maintain communications in class E airspace (although it is usually sensible to do so).

Figure AL5.6
The key characteristics of different classes of Controlled Airspace.

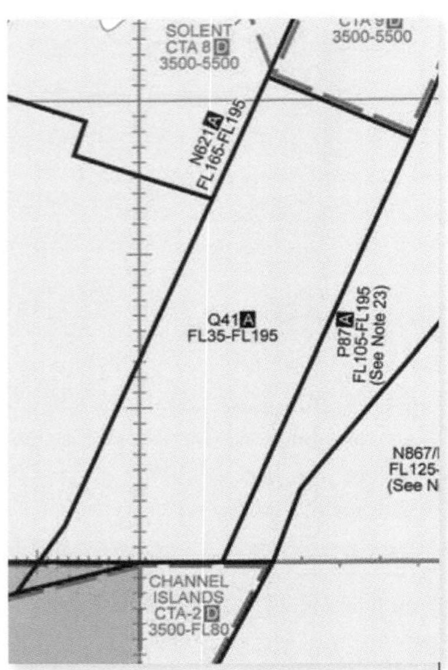

Figure AL5.7
An airway designated Q41, it is Class A airspace and so entry is prohibited to VFR flights. In the section between the Solent CTA and the Channel Islands CTA the base of the airway is Flight Level (FL35).

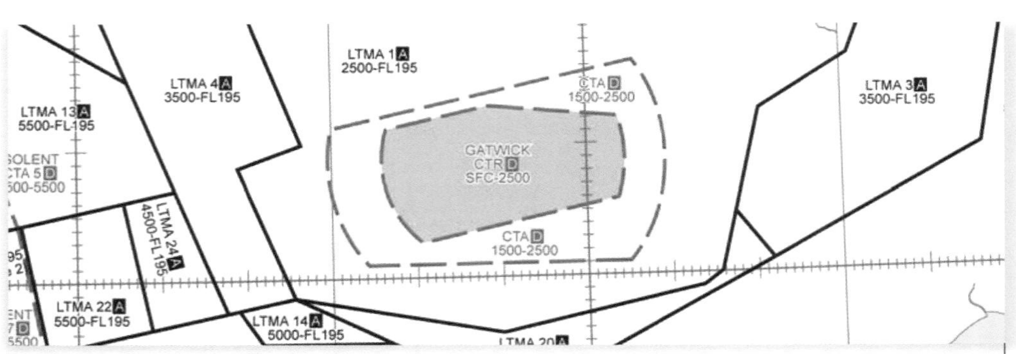

Figure AL5.8
Controlled airspace in the vicinity of London Gatwick airport. There is a class D control zone (CTR) from the surface to 2,500ft amsl, a class D control area (CTA) from 1,500ft amsl to 2,500ft amsl and above the London TMA (LTMA) which is class A airspace with a base of 2,500ft amsl.

Figure AL5.9
VFR Flight in Controlled Airspace.

The following table summarises the characteristics of controlled airspace in relation to VFR flight:

Airspace Class	Entry permission required?	Continuous communications required	Air traffic control service provided	ATC separation from other flights?
Class A	VFR flight not permitted	VFR flight not permitted	VFR flight not permitted	VFR flight not permitted
Class B	Yes	Yes	Yes	Yes
Class C	Yes	Yes	Yes	VFR flights separated from IFR flights, receive traffic information on other VFR flights, traffic avoidance advice on request
Class D	Yes	Yes	Yes	VFR flights receive traffic information on all other flights, traffic avoidance advice available on request
Class E	No	No	No	No

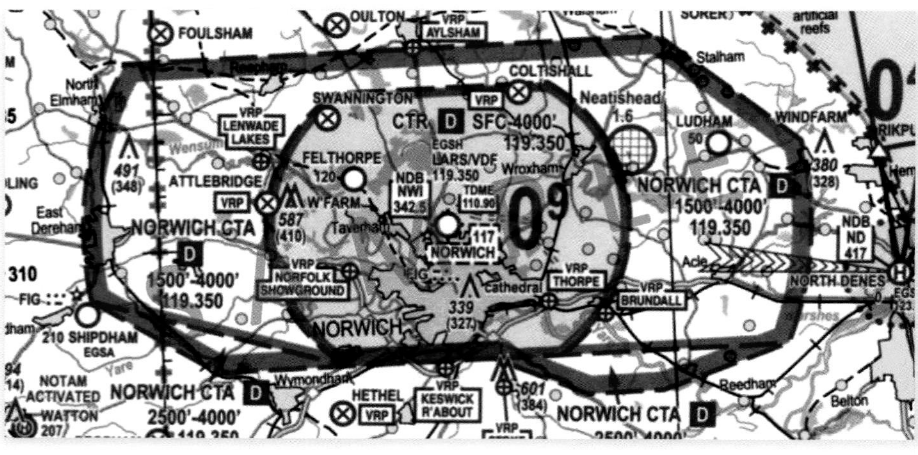

Figure AL5.10
A CTR and CTAs around and above Norwich airport in the UK, as depicted on a VFR aeronautical chart.

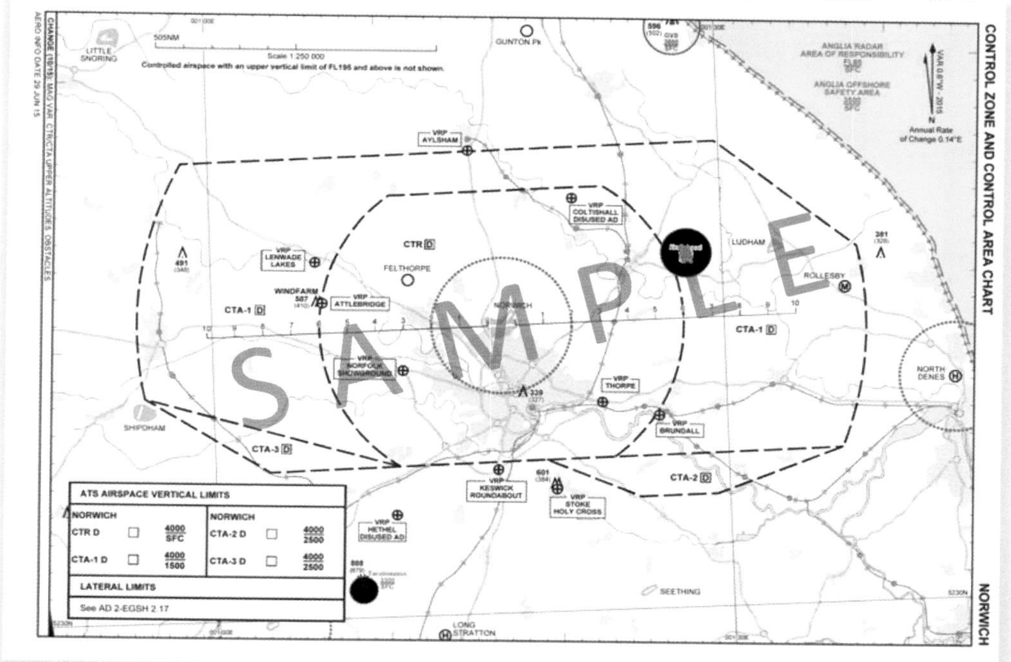

Figure AL5.11
The Norwich CTR and CTAs as depicted on a chart in the UK AIP. Note the box describing the vertical limits of the control zone (CTR) and each of the control areas (CTAs).

Full details of each area of controlled airspace, including dimensions, airspace class, operating procedures, contact frequencies etc. are published by each country in a document known as the 'Aeronautical Information Publication' (AIP), which is described in more detail in a later section. In terms of airspace, the appropriate country's 'AIP' should be considered as the authoritative source of information.

In practice, it often seems that pilots of VFR flights actively avoid flying through even those classes of controlled airspace (classes B to E) in which VFR flight is permitted. This can lead to VFR flights making longer routings than necessary or passing through so-called 'choke points' where aircraft seeking to avoid controlled airspace are funnelled into relatively narrow gaps, particularly between CTRs. None of this should be necessary as in practice ATC are usually very accommodating to VFR flights wishing to cross areas of controlled airspace, even around busy airports. The key is to understand the rules and procedures that apply to VFR flight in controlled airspace, and to know any specific routings or crossing procedures for a particular area of controlled airspace.

In the case of control zones (CTR) in particular, there are often local arrangements that allow, for example, aircraft to operate from smaller airfields or airstrips within the CTR without complying with all the requirements of the CTR – for example the requirement to contact the control zone ATC unit. These arrangements are often very useful, for example where there is a smaller airfield situated close to the edge of a CTR, to allow VFR flights to operate in a defined area around an airfield without the need to seek permission to enter the CTR. Any such local arrangements may be published in the AIP or on an airfield's website. When describing such arrangements, it is common to refer to a 'Local Flying Zone' (LFZ), a 'Local Flying Area' (LFA), a 'Letter Of Agreement' (LOA) or a 'Memorandum of Understanding' (MOU). It is the pilot's responsibility to check the details and validity of any such arrangements and adhere to the restrictions and procedures they specify.

Figure AL5.12
A full description of the Norwich CTR and CTAs in the UK AIP.

EGSH AD 2.17 AIR TRAFFIC SERVICES AIRSPACE

Designation and lateral limits	Vertical Limits	Airspace Class	ATS unit callsign/ language	Transition Altitude	Remarks
1	2	3	4	5	6
NORWICH CTR 524530N 0011035E - 524536N 0012308E - thence clockwise by the arc of a circle radius 6 nm centered on 524034N 0011747E to 523537N 0012319E - 523531N 0011049E - thence clockwise by the arc of a circle radius 6 nm centered on 524033N 0011609E to 524530N 0011035E	Upper limit: 4000 ft ALT Lower limit: SFC	D	NORWICH APPROACH English	5000 ft	
NORWICH CTA 1 524653N 0005826E - 524708N 0012946E - 524304N 0013754E - thence clockwise by the arc of a circle radius 12.5 nm centered on 524034N 0011747E to 523541N 0013639E - 523537N 0012319E - thence anti-clockwise by the arc of a circle radius 6 nm centered on 524034N 0011747E to 524536N 0012308E - 524530N 0011035E - thence anti-clockwise by the arc of a circle radius 6 nm centered on 524033N 0011609E to 523531N 0011049E - 523815N 0005559E - thence clockwise by the arc of a circle radius 12.5 nm centered on 524033N 0011609E to 524653N 0005826E	Upper limit: 4000 ft ALT Lower limit: 1500 ft ALT	D	NORWICH APPROACH English	5000 ft	
NORWICH CTA 2 523535N 0011921E - 523541N 0013639E - 523409N 0012916E - 523407N 0012448E - 523535N 0011921E	Upper limit: 4000 ft ALT Lower limit: 2500 ft ALT	D	NORWICH APPROACH English	5000 ft	
NORWICH CTA 3 523815N 0005559E - 523531N 0011049E - 523527N 0010311E - 523815N 0005559E	Upper limit: 4000 ft ALT Lower limit: 2500 ft ALT	D	NORWICH APPROACH English	5000 ft	
NORWICH ATZ A circle, 2.5 nm radius centred at 524033N 0011658E on longest notified runway (09/27)	Upper limit: 2000 ft Lower limit: SFC	D	NORWICH APPROACH English	5000 ft	

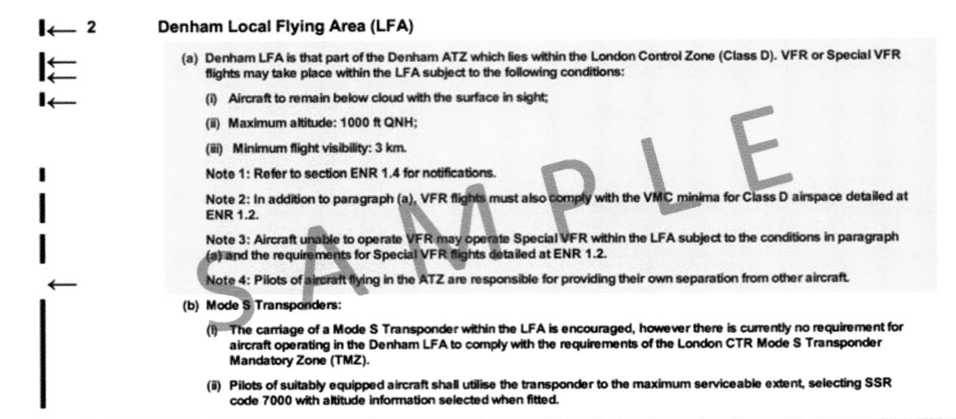

2 **Denham Local Flying Area (LFA)**

(a) Denham LFA is that part of the Denham ATZ which lies within the London Control Zone (Class D). VFR or Special VFR flights may take place within the LFA subject to the following conditions:

(i) Aircraft to remain below cloud with the surface in sight;

(ii) Maximum altitude: 1000 ft QNH;

(iii) Minimum flight visibility: 3 km.

Note 1: Refer to section ENR 1.4 for notifications.

Note 2: In addition to paragraph (a), VFR flights must also comply with the VMC minima for Class D airspace detailed at ENR 1.2.

Note 3: Aircraft unable to operate VFR may operate Special VFR within the LFA subject to the conditions in paragraph (a) and the requirements for Special VFR flights detailed at ENR 1.2.

Note 4: Pilots of aircraft flying in the ATZ are responsible for providing their own separation from other aircraft.

(b) Mode S Transponders:

(i) The carriage of a Mode S Transponder within the LFA is encouraged, however there is currently no requirement for aircraft operating in the Denham LFA to comply with the requirements of the London CTR Mode S Transponder Mandatory Zone (TMZ).

(ii) Pilots of suitably equipped aircraft shall utilise the transponder to the maximum serviceable extent, selecting SSR code 7000 with altitude information selected when fitted.

Figure AL5.13
Procedures for the Denham Local Flying Area (LFA) in the UK AIP

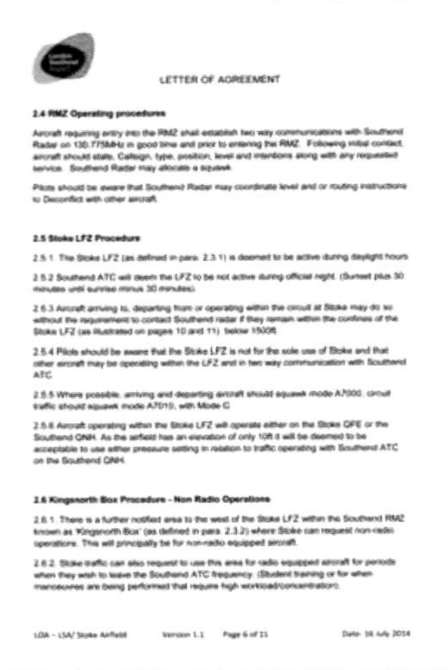

LETTER OF AGREEMENT

2.4 RMZ Operating procedures

Aircraft requiring entry into the RMZ shall establish two way communications with Southend Radar on 130.775MHz in good time and prior to entering the RMZ. Following initial contact, aircraft should state, Callsign, type, position, level and intentions along with any requested service. Southend Radar may allocate a squawk.

Pilots should be aware that Southend Radar may coordinate level and or routing instructions to Deconflict with other aircraft.

2.5 Stoke LFZ Procedure

2.5.1 The Stoke LFZ (as defined in para. 2.3.1) is deemed to be active during daylight hours.

2.5.2 Southend ATC will deem the LFZ to be not active during official night. (Sunset plus 30 minutes until sunrise minus 30 minutes)

2.5.3 Aircraft arriving to, departing from or operating within the circuit at Stoke may do so without the requirement to contact Southend radar if they remain within the confines of the Stoke LFZ (as illustrated on pages 10 and 11) below 1500ft.

2.5.4 Pilots should be aware that the Stoke LFZ is not for the sole use of Stoke and that other aircraft may be operating within the LFZ and in two way communication with Southend ATC.

2.5.5 Where possible, arriving and departing aircraft should squawk mode A7000, circuit traffic should squawk mode A7010, with Mode C.

2.5.6 Aircraft operating within the Stoke LFZ will operate either on the Stoke QFE or the Southend QNH. As the airfield has an elevation of only 10ft it will be deemed to be acceptable to use either pressure setting in relation to traffic operating with Southend ATC on the Southend QNH.

2.6 Kingsnorth Box Procedure - Non Radio Operations

2.6.1 There is a further notified area to the west of the Stoke LFZ within the Southend RMZ known as 'Kingsnorth Box' (as defined in para. 2.3.2) where Stoke can request non-radio operations. This will principally be for non-radio equipped aircraft.

2.6.2 Stoke traffic can also request to use this area for radio equipped aircraft for periods when they wish to leave the Southend ATC frequency. (Student training or for when manoeuvres are being performed that require high workload/concentration).

LOA - LSA/ Stoke Airfield Version 1.1 Page 6 of 11 Date: 16 July 2014

Figure AL5.14
A Letter of Agreement relating to operations from a small airfield situated within controlled airspace.

Controlled airspace is established mostly to allow ATC to create an area where they can control and separate aircraft, however there may be other reasons for restricting flights in certain areas. In addition to controlled airspace, there may be areas of **notified airspace**, usually established by a state to keep aircraft away from hazards or to protect an area or installation on the surface. There are three principle types of notified airspace:

Prohibited area	Airspace of defined dimensions within which the flight of aircraft is prohibited.
Restricted area	Airspace of defined dimensions, within which the flight of aircraft is restricted in accordance with certain specified conditions.
Danger area	Airspace of defined dimensions within which activities dangerous to aircraft may exist.

Figure AL5.15
The three principle types of notified airspace.

Figure AL5.16
Prohibited areas are often associated with locations that are involved in national security – in this case the Atomic Weapons Establishment in the UK.

A prohibited area will be marked on an aeronautical chart using a specific designator for the area starting with the letter 'P'. The chart will show the vertical extent of the prohibited area and as with controlled airspace, the exact dimensions of a prohibited area and any associated information will be found in the appropriate AIP.

A restricted area will be marked on an aeronautical chart including a specific designator for the area starting with the letter 'R'. The chart will show the vertical extent of a restricted area and full details of a restricted area will be found in the AIP. Sometimes a restricted area applies only to certain classes of aircraft – for example helicopters or microlights. Additionally, flight within a restricted area may be permitted subject to certain conditions – again full details will be given in the AIP.

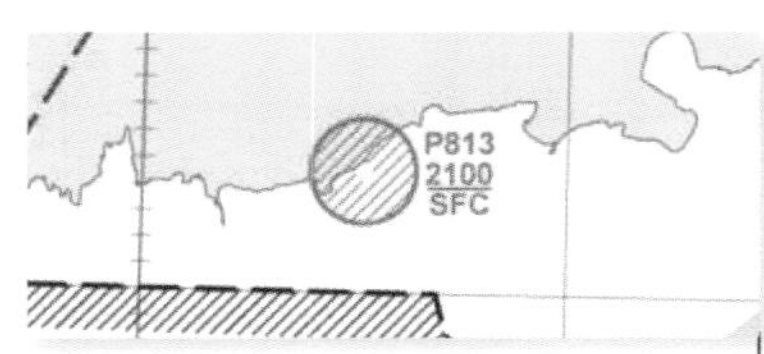

Figure AL5.17
Prohibited area P813 in northern Scotland as depicted on a chart in the UK Aeronautical Information Publication (AIP). It extends from the surface to 2100ft amsl.

ENR 5.1 PROHIBITED, RESTRICTED AND DANGER AREAS (continued)

Identification and Name Lateral Limits	Upper Limit Lower Limit	Remarks (time of activity, type of restriction, nature of hazard, risk of interception)
1	2	3
Prohibited Area		
EG P047 WINFRITH A circle, 1 nm radius centred at 504052N 0021535W	Upper limit: 1000 ft ALT Lower limit: SFC	SI 2007/1929.
EG P106 HARWELL A circle, 2 nm radius centred at 513430N 0011905W	Upper limit: 2500 ft ALT Lower limit: SFC	Flight permitted for the purpose of landing at or taking off from the helicopter landing area at Harwell, with the permission of the person in charge of the installation and in accordance with any conditions to which that permission is subject. SI 2007/1929.
EG P611 COULPORT / FASLANE A circle, 2 nm radius centred at 560331N 0045159W	Upper limit: 2200 ft ALT Lower limit: SFC	SI 2007/1929.
EG P813 DOUNREAY A circle, 2 nm radius centred at 583435N 0034434W	Upper limit: 2100 ft ALT Lower limit: SFC	SI 2007/1929.

Figure AL5.18
A list of UK prohibited areas in the UK AIP.

Figure AL5.19
Restricted areas may be associated with prisons and other sensitive government or military installations.

EG R322 WYLFA A circle, 2 nm radius centred at 532458N 0042852W	Upper limit: 2100 ft ALT Lower limit: SFC	Flight permitted at a height of not less than 2000 ft above ground level whilst operating under and in accordance with a clearance from the air traffic control unit at RAF Valley. Flight permitted for the purpose of landing at or taking off from the helicopter landing area at Wylfa, with the permission of the person in charge of the installation and in accordance with any conditions to which that permission is subject. SI 2007/1929.

Figure AL5.20
Details of UK restricted area R322 in the UK AIP.

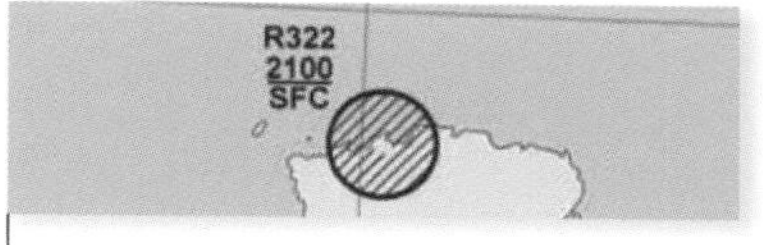

Figure AL5.21
Restricted area R322 as depicted on a UK AIP chart, it extends from the surface to 2100ft amsl.

A danger area will be marked on an aeronautical chart including a specific designator for the area starting with the letter 'D'. Of all notified airspace, danger areas tend to be the most common and cover the largest areas. Danger areas are often associated with military activity such as weapons ranges and military training areas. Other hazards that may be encountered within danger areas include missile firings, tethered balloons, free-fall parachuting (day and night), aircraft towing targets, unmanned aircraft, anti-aircraft weapon firing, etc. None of these activities are compatible with safe flight for a non-participating aircraft which is, of course, precisely why a danger area is established in the first place.

Figure AL5.22
Firing of live ammunition is the type of activity which may take place within a danger area.

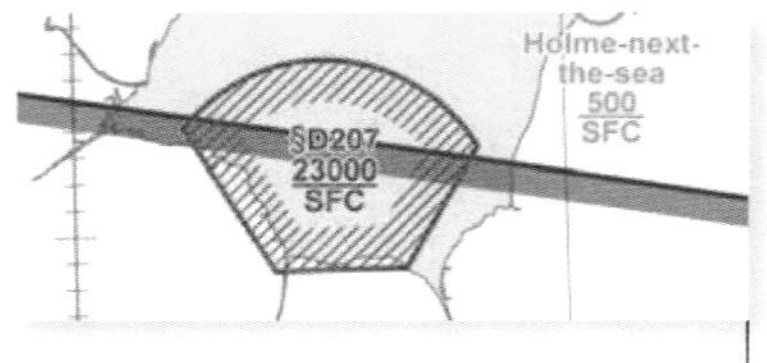

Figure AL5.23
Danger area D207 as depicted on a chart in the UK AIP, it extends from the surface to 23,000ft amsl.

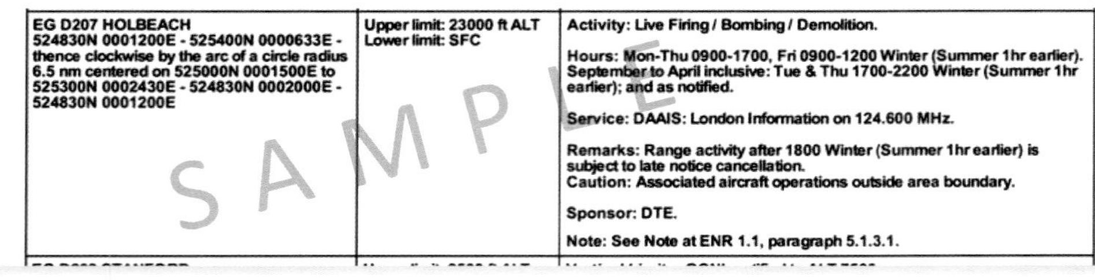

EG D207 HOLBEACH 524830N 0001200E - 525400N 0000633E - thence clockwise by the arc of a circle radius 6.5 nm centered on 525000N 0001500E to 525300N 0002430E - 524830N 0002000E - 524830N 0001200E	Upper limit: 23000 ft ALT Lower limit: SFC	Activity: Live Firing / Bombing / Demolition. Hours: Mon-Thu 0900-1700, Fri 0900-1200 Winter (Summer 1hr earlier). September to April inclusive: Tue & Thu 1700-2200 Winter (Summer 1hr earlier); and as notified. Service: DAAIS: London Information on 124.600 MHz. Remarks: Range activity after 1800 Winter (Summer 1hr earlier) is subject to late notice cancellation. Caution: Associated aircraft operations outside area boundary. Sponsor: DTE. Note: See Note at ENR 1.1, paragraph 5.1.3.1.

Figure AL5.24
Details of danger area D207 in the UK AIP, including activity times and a contact frequency for obtaining more information about activity in the danger area.

An aeronautical chart will show the vertical extent of a danger area and details of the danger area will be found in the AIP. Danger areas in particular may be active only on certain days and at certain times and there may be services to give information on the status of a danger area or to provide a crossing service.

Visual signals may be used to warn unauthorised aircraft that they are flying in, or about to enter, a restricted, prohibited or danger area. This signal is a series of projectiles launched from the ground at 10 second intervals, bursting into red and green lights or stars. An aircraft that sees such a signal is to take such corrective action as may be necessary.

Individual states may also have other types of airspace relating to specific hazards or activities, details of which will be found in the state's AIP.

In some European states, the immediate vicinity of some aerodromes may be protected by an area known as an **Aerodrome Traffic Zone** (**ATZ**). In essence, a flight wishing to operate within an ATZ is required to make contact with the Air Traffic Service at the aerodrome. Full details on the dimensions of an ATZ and operating procedures (which may vary between different states) will be found in the appropriate AIP.

Uncontrolled Airspace

Airspace that is not controlled is, not surprisingly, known as uncontrolled airspace. Uncontrolled airspace may be either Class F or G. The principle characteristics of each class of uncontrolled airspace in relation to a VFR flight are:

Class F	ATC entry clearance not required, continuous communications not necessary although all flights receive a flight information service if requested.
Class G	No entry or communications requirements, although all flights can request a flight information service.

Figure AL5.25
The main characteristics of uncontrolled airspace in relation to VFR flight.

In Class F and G airspace, there is a general speed restriction of no more than 250 knots indicated airspeed (IAS) when below 10,000ft above mean sea level (amsl).

In practice, class F airspace (sometimes called 'advisory airspace' in relation to IFR flights) is largely being phased out in Europe and replaced with one of the other classes of airspace.

VFR flight in class G airspace is the least restricted flight possible in terms of ATC laison, maintaining radio communications, pilot licencing, aircraft equipment etc. However, precisely because of this freedom – meaning that Class G airspace is open to many different aircraft, pilots and activities, without the need to communicate with anyone or be aware of each other – a pilot in Class G airspace must be actutely aware that other aircraft may well be operating close by at any time. The most effective defence against a close encounter with other aircraft in these circumstances is to maintain a good lookout at all times, which is precisely why flight instructors spend so much time teaching lookout and reminding their students to lookout.

Radio Mandatory Zones (RMZ)

A **Radio Mandatory Zone** (**RMZ**) is airspace within which *"...the carriage and operation of radio equipment is mandatory"*.

An RMZ does not have its own airspace classification, so the Visual Flight Rules which apply are those of the airspace class (E, F or G) within which the RMZ is established. RMZs usually exist where classes A to D airspace would be too restrictive or cannot be justified, but some other factor (for example, an airfield outside controlled airspace with intensive IFR activity) means that radio contact with ATC will significantly aid flight safety.

An RMZ will be marked on aeronautical charts and the pilot of a VFR flight wishing to operate within an RMZ is required to establish two-way communication on the appropriate radio frequency. The Standardised European Rules of the Air (SERA) do not define the term 'two-way communication', but they do require that before entering an RMZ, a pilot must make an initial call on the appropriate radio frequency containing the following information:

- the designation of the ATC unit being called;
- aircraft radio call sign, aircraft type;
- position;
- level;
- the intentions of the flight;
- any other information the 'competent authority' requires to be given.

Once inside an RMZ, a flight is required to maintain a continuous air-ground voice communication watch, in other words listen out on the appropriate radio frequency and not leave that frequency whilst within the RMZ.

In certain circumstances, for example where there is an aerodrome without an ATC unit located inside an RMZ, or near the edge of an RMZ, there may be special arrangements in place to allow flights to operate to and from that aerodrome without complying with the two-way communications and continuous watch requirements of the RMZ. Such local arrangements are quite common and they may be notified in the AIP. Alternatively, especially if they involve a small airstrip or private landing site, they may not be well publicised and it will be necessary to contact the airfield concerned, or the ATC unit responsible for the RMZ, to get details of any such arrangement or to obtain permission to operate in an RMZ without complying with the radio communication requirements. In any event, it is the responsibility of the pilot in command to be aware of any such special arrangements and operate in accordance with them.

Transponder Mandatory Zones (TMZ)

A **Transponder Mandatory Zone** (**TMZ**) is airspace where the carriage and operation of a pressure-altitude reporting transponder is mandatory.

A **transponder** is essentially a radio which transmits data to ATC. At its most basic, a transponder transmits a four figure code which the pilot has set on the transponder. On a suitably-equipped radar screen, this code shows the aircraft's position to ATC. Most modern transponders are also capable of transmitting the aircraft's level to ATC, this altitude-reporting capability of a transponder is known as 'Mode C' and may be indicated on the transponder itself as a selection marked 'ALT'.

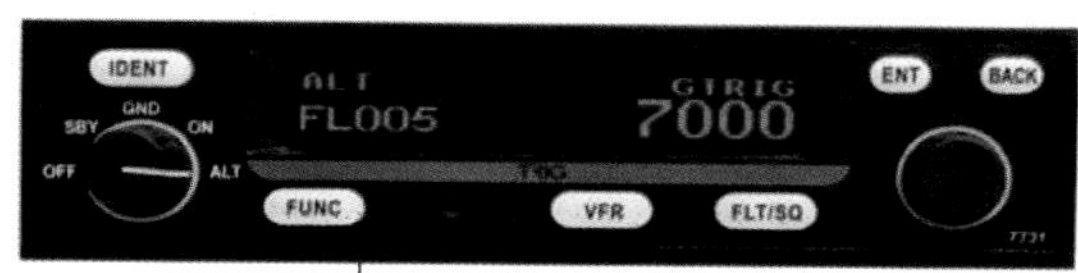

Figure AL5.26

A typical transponder for a general aviation aircraft, in this case the transponder shows the four-digit code selected by the pilot and the 'pressure altitude' (or 'Flight Level') being measured and transmitted by the transponder.

Any flight operating within a TMZ must carry and operate a transponder with altitude reporting capability, so that ATC can see on radar what aircraft are inside the TMZ and at what level they are flying. TMZs are sometimes established underneath controlled airspace, so that ATC will be alerted automatically if an aircraft 'infringes' controlled airspace by flying too high. Other than the transponder operation requirement, a TMZ does not have its own airspace classification but adopts the rules of the airspace it is located within.

TMZs are depicted on aeronautical charts and detailed in the AIP. Flight in a TMZ does not require ATC clearance provided the aircraft is equipped with, and operating, a suitable transponder. Furthermore, flight in a TMZ does not require voice communications with ATC, although it may advisable to do so. At its discretion, an ATC unit may permit a non-transponder equipped aircraft to operate within a TMZ, subject to obtaining permission prior to entering the TMZ. As is the case with RMZs, local arrangements may apply to allow certain flights to operate within the TMZ without complying with the transponder operation requirements.

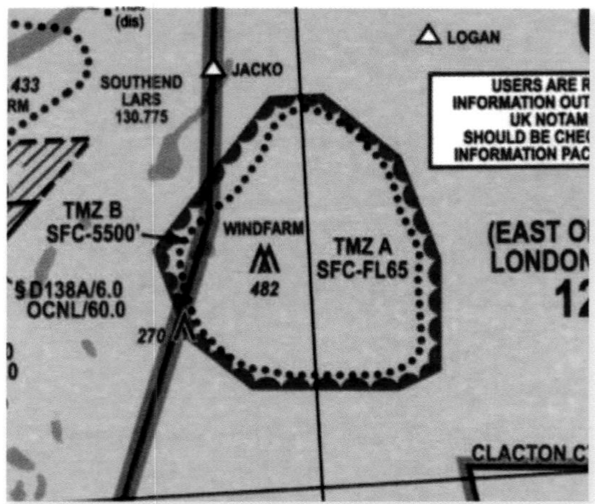

Figure AL5.27
A Transponder Mandatory Zone (TMZ) as depicted on a VFR aeronautical chart.

Progress Check

45. Name one class of controlled airspace.
46. What is the generic term for airspace within which an air traffic control service is provided?
47. What are the three main requirements for a VFR flight wishing to operate in controlled airspace?
48. What is a CTA?
49. What is a CTR?
50. Is VFR flight permitted in all classes of controlled airspace?
51. What type of airspace is indicated by the designation 'R' – for example R311?
52. Where can the pilot find full details of a danger area?
53. What is an ATZ?
54. What is the least 'restrictive' class of uncontrolled airspace?
55. What is an 'RMZ'?
56. What specific item of aircraft equipment must be operated for flight within a 'TMZ'?

These questions are intended to test knowledge and reinforce some of the key learning points from this section. In answering these questions, a 'pass rate' of around 80% should be the target.

Model answers are found at page 145

Intentionally Left Blank

AL6 Altimeter Setting Procedures

Height, altitude and flight level

VFR altimeter setting procedures

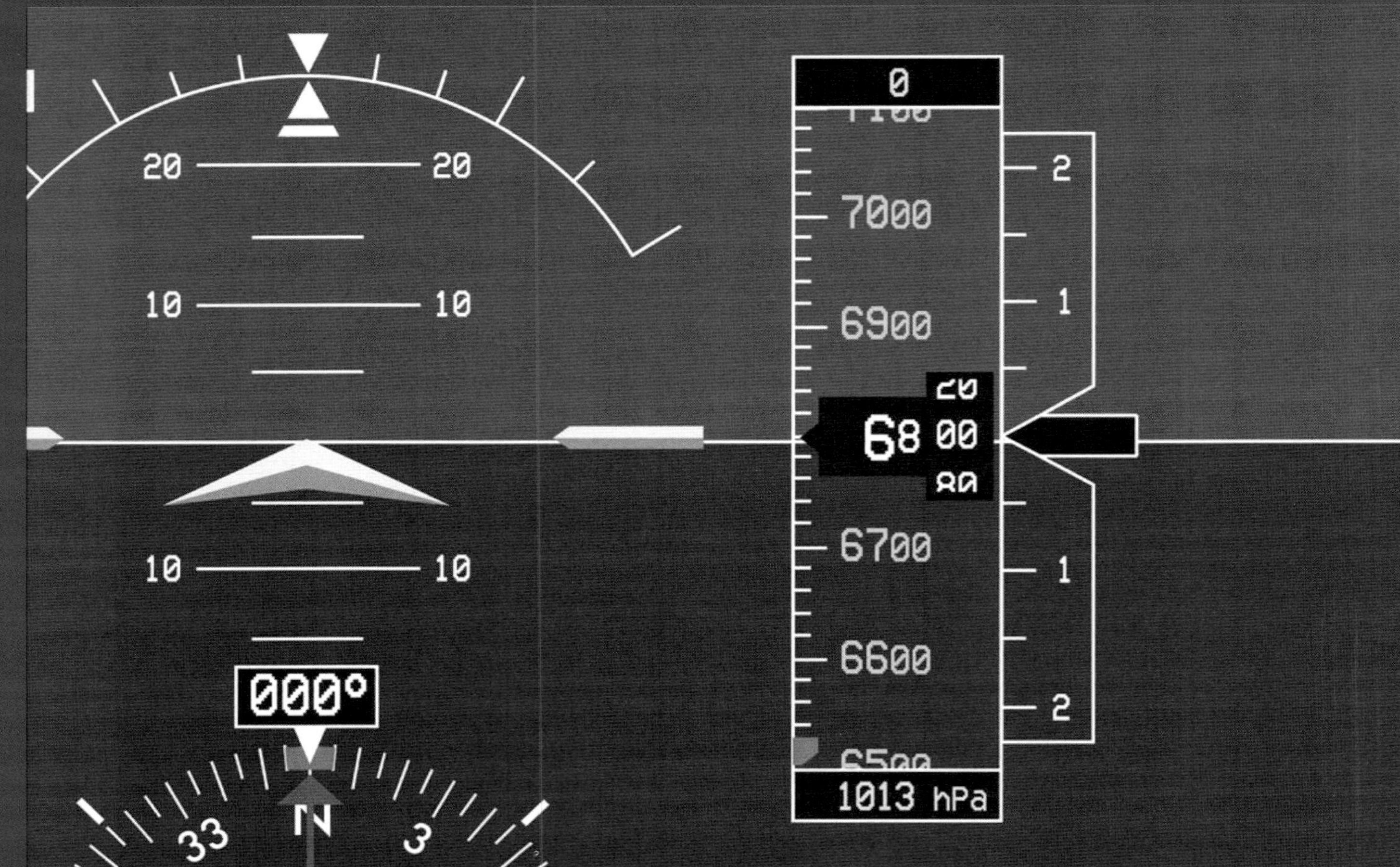

AL6 Altimeter Setting Procedures

Height, altitude and flight level

Vertical navigation in all VFR flying (and virtually all IFR flying) is carried out by reference to the humble pressure altimeter, one of the simplest aircraft instruments and one found on virtually every flying machine, from the smallest single seat microlight to the largest airliner.

At its core, an altimeter is nothing more than a 'barometer' – an instrument that measures pressure. Atmospheric pressure reduces as height increases, and it does so at a predictable rate. An altimeter makes use of this fact by measuring atmospheric pressure and displaying it in the form of a vertical distance (usually, but not always, in units of 'feet').

Figure AL6.1
A 'round dial' altimeter with the pointed hands indicating hundreds (long pointer) and thousands (short pointer) of feet, in this case indicating just over 9,000 feet.

Figure AL6.2
On this electronic cockpit display, vertical distance is indicated inside the box which points to the markings on the vertical tape, in this case indicating 6800 feet.

The vertical distance displayed on an altimeter can be expressed in one of three ways:

Height	Vertical distance above a specified point on the surface, usually an airfield/landing site or a runway threshold.
Altitude	Vertical distance 'above mean sea level' (amsl).
Flight Level	Vertical distance above a universal standard pressure level.

Figure AL6.3
The three datum for defining vertical distance.

QFE
Altimeter indicates
HEIGHT above a
fixed point on the surface
(usually an airfiield)

QNH
Altimeter indicates
ALTITUDE
Above Mean Sea Level **(AMSL)**

Standard Setting
Altimeter indicates
FLIGHT LEVEL (FL)
above the 1013 pressure datum

1000ft
HEIGHT
1000ft
2000ft
ALTITUDE
2000ft
FL40
FLIGHT LEVEL
4000ft
1013 hPa

Figure AL6.4

HEIGHT = vertical distance above a specific point on the surface

ALTITUDE = vertical distance above mean sea level (amsl)

FLIGHT LEVEL =vertical distance above the universal standard pressure level

Because atmospheric pressure is constantly changing, the altimeter must have a means adjusting the altimeter reading by applying the appropriate 'pressure setting', so that the altimeter gives an accurate reading based on the current atmospheric pressure. This is done by setting the appropriate pressure setting in the altimeter's pressure setting 'window' (sometimes referred to as the 'sub-scale' window). Within Europe the standard aviation unit for measuring and setting atmospheric pressure is the 'hectopascal' (hPa). The hectopascal replaced the 'millibar' (mb), but fortunately in practical terms the only difference is the term used, as 1hPa = 1mb. However, many altimeters have pressure setting windows marked in 'mb'.

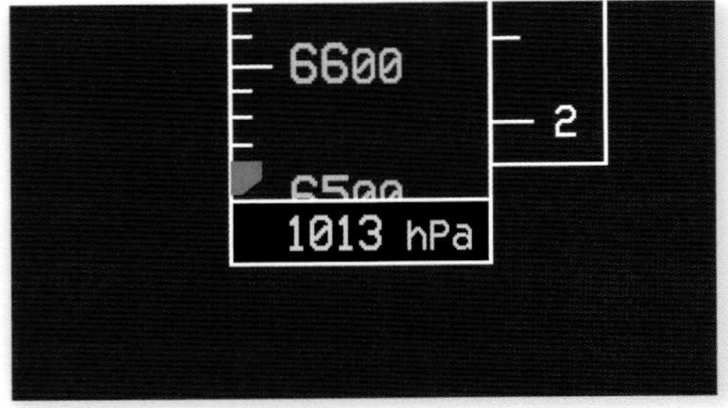

Figure AL6.5
The altimeter sub-scale allows the pilot to select the datum from which vertical distance is being measured.

It is important to repeat that the altimeter measures pressure, and displays pressure in the form of a vertical distance. Thus, when an aircraft is flying at a constant level as indicated on the altimeter, it is actually flying at a constant pressure level.

To illustrate the point, imagine an aircraft flying from an area of high pressure to an area of low pressure. If the altimeter is indicating an 'altitude' of 1800ft where the sea-level pressure in the high-pressure area is 1020 hectopascals (hPa), the aircraft is flying at a 'pressure level' of around 960hPa. (Because air pressure reduces with increasing altitude at a rate of about 1hPa per 30 feet; 1800ft ÷ 30 is 60hPa). So what happens if the aircraft flies towards an area of lower pressure without changing the pressure setting on the altimeter? Sea-level pressure will be lower in the area of low pressure, so the 960hPa pressure level will be closer to the surface. This means that even though the aircraft is still flying at an indicated altitude of 1800ft, if the altimeter pressure setting has not been changed the aircraft will actually be closer to the surface. If the pressure at sea level in the area of low pressure is 990hPa, for example, the aircraft will be around 900ft lower than indicated on the altimeter. Obviously this is not safe.

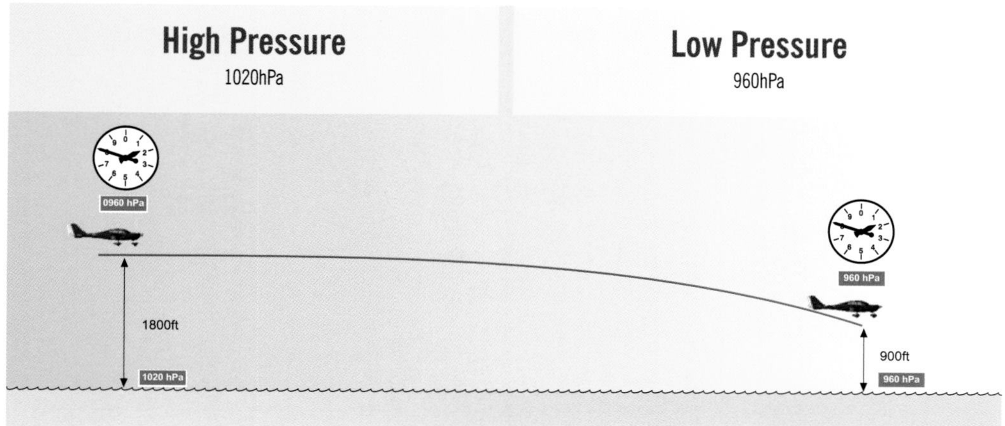

Figure AL6.6
"High to Low, Down You Go".

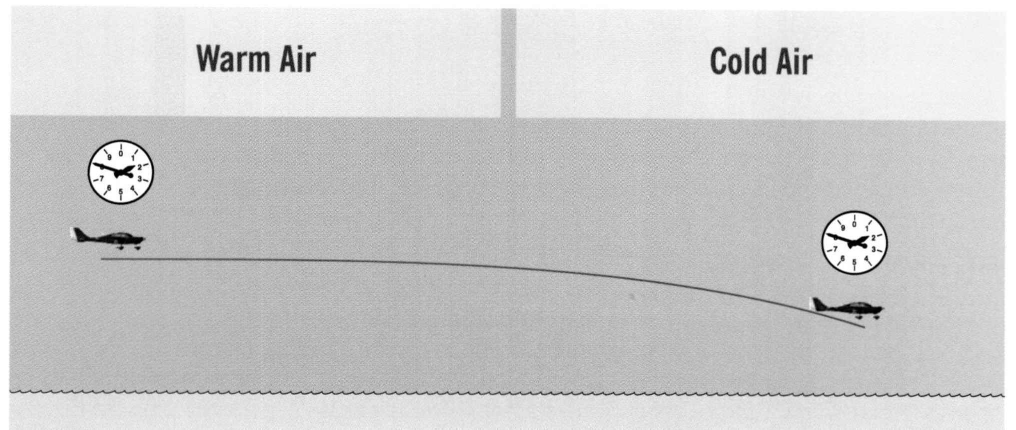

Figure AL6.7
"High to Low, Down You Go".

Something similar happens if the aircraft flies from an area where the temperature is warm to one where it is colder. Cold air is more dense than warm air, and so any given pressure level is lower in cold air than in warm air.

The effect of flying from high pressure to low pressure, or high temperature to low temperature, is summarised in the maxim: *"High to low, Down you go"*.

In order for the altimeter to display the required type of vertical distance (height, altitude or Flight Level), the appropriate pressure setting must be set. The three types of pressure setting, and the related vertical distance, are:

QFE	Altimeter reads **height**
QNH	Altimeter reads **altitude**
Standard Pressure	Altimeter reads **Flight Level**. The Standard Pressure is 1013 hectopascals (hPa) and is very occasionally referred to as 'QNE'

Figure AL6.8
The key pressure settings used to define vertical distance.

Figure AL6.9
QFE Altimeter reads 'height'
QNH Altimeter reads 'altitude'
Standard Pressure Altimeter reads 'Flight Level'.

Because of the importance of using the correct altimeter setting, pilots and controllers should never refer to a pressure setting in terms of a figure alone, but instead a pressure setting should always be preceded by the appropriate 'Q' code, for example, *"QNH 1020"* or *"QFE 1005"*.

In summary:

Figure AL6.10
A summary of the three altimeter settings, the related terms and definitions.

Pressure Setting	Term	Description
QFE	**Height**	Altimeter reads height **above a fixed point on the surface**
QNH	**Altitude**	Altimeter reads altitude **above mean sea level**
Standard Pressure	**Flight Level**	Altimeter reads Flight Level **above the 1013 hPa pressure level**

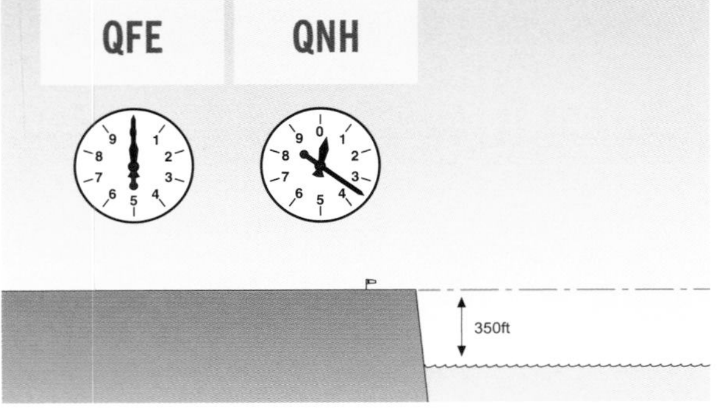

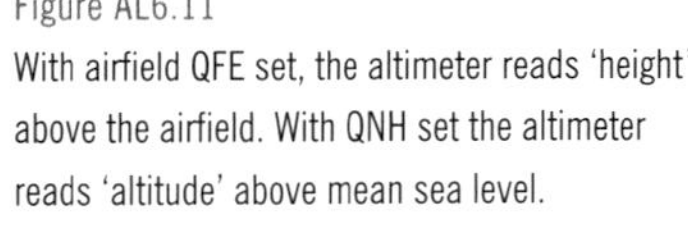
Figure AL6.11
With airfield QFE set, the altimeter reads 'height' above the airfield. With QNH set the altimeter reads 'altitude' above mean sea level.

To see how this works in practice, imagine an aircraft parked on the apron of an aerodrome. If the pilot sets the airfield QFE on the altimeter, the altimeter should read zero, or very close to zero, as the aircraft is on the surface of the airfield. If the pilot now sets the airfield QNH on the altimeter, it will indicate the vertical distance above sea level. So, if the airfield apron is situated 350 feet above mean sea level, the altimeter should read about 350 feet. The vertical distance above sea level of an airfield, or any point on the surface, can be described as its **elevation**. So, if an airfield is described as having an 'elevation' of 350ft, it is 350 feet above mean sea level. Airfield elevation (defined as the highest point of the landing area) is marked on aeronautical charts and listed in the AIP and commercially-produced flight guides. If there is a significant variation in elevation across an airfield (ie if it is on a slope), different elevations may be listed in the AIP for the apron and the runway thresholds. The altimeter should be checked on the ground, before flight, to ensure not only that the altimeter is operating correctly and giving an accurate reading, but also to ensure that the correct pressure setting has been applied.

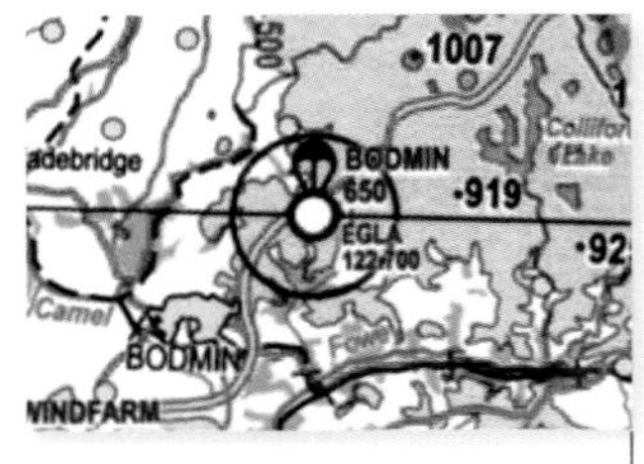

Figure AL6.12
On this VFR aeronautical chart the elevation of Bodmin airfield is noted as 650 feet amsl.

EGLA	
650ft 21hPa	3.5nm NE of Bodmin N5029.98 W00439.95
	Bodmin

Figure AL6.13
In this VFR Flight Guide the elevation of Bodmin airfield, and the equivalent hPa difference, is shown.

If the aircraft now goes flying, with airfield QFE set on the altimeter, the altimeter will indicate 'height' above the airfield. This may be quite different from the vertical distance to the surface directly underneath the aircraft. If QNH is set on the altimeter, it will now read 'altitude' above mean sea level, but the actual vertical distance to the surface underneath the aircraft will depend on the elevation of that surface.

Because atmospheric pressure is constantly changing, the values of QNH and QFE will vary with time and location (the Standard Pressure always remains the same). For this reason, as already illustrated, it is important to keep the altimeter setting updated throughout a flight in order for the altimeter to give an accurate reading.

Although most states around the world use 'feet' to measure altitude in aviation, there are certain states (for example China and Russia) which measure altitude in metres. Additionally, although 'hectopascals' are the aviation-standard units for altimeter settings, some states (for example, the USA) use inches of mercury and just to be different a few states use millimetres of mercury.

CLERMONT FERRAND AUVERGNE
AD2 LFLC APP 01

ALT AD : 1092 (39 hPa) LAT : 45 47 09 N LONG : 003 09 45 E	**LFLC** VAR : 0° (10)

VDF : 122.225 - 118.625

Figure AL6.14
This French AIP aerodrome chart for Clermont Ferrand shows that the airfield elevation is 1092ft, equivalent to 39 hectopascals (hPa).

VFR altimeter setting procedures

The following is a general guide to altimeter setting procedures for a VFR flight. The aircraft operator, local procedures or regional procedures may dictate specific altimeter setting procedures, which will over-rule this general guidance.

Before flight, the altimeter can be checked on the ground by setting the airfield QNH and checking the altimeter reading against the known airfield elevation. ICAO recommends that a 'tolerance' of plus or minus 60ft should be considered acceptable in an altimeter reading.

When taking-off at an airfield outside controlled airspace, any desired pressure setting can be used. At an airfield inside controlled airspace, at least one altimeter should be set to airfield QNH. An aircraft taking off from an airfield beneath a TMA or Control Area (CTA) should use QNH. If the aircraft is staying within the visual circuit (traffic pattern) at the airfield of departure, airfield QFE may be used.

Once an aircraft has left the vicinity of the departure airfield, QNH is the normal altimeter setting when flying at or below the 'transition altitude'. This term needs further explanation, so here are a couple of important definitions:

Transition Altitude	The altitude at and below which the level of the aircraft is controlled by reference to 'altitude' (that is, QNH is set on the altimeter)
Transition Level	The lowest useable Flight Level above the transition altitude

Figure AL6.15
The definition of Transition Altitude and Transition Level.

Although a VFR flight may use QNH when flying outside controlled airspace, even when above the Transition Altitude, even VFR flights are recommended to use the Standard Pressure (and thus fly at a 'Flight Level') if cruising above the Transition Altitude.

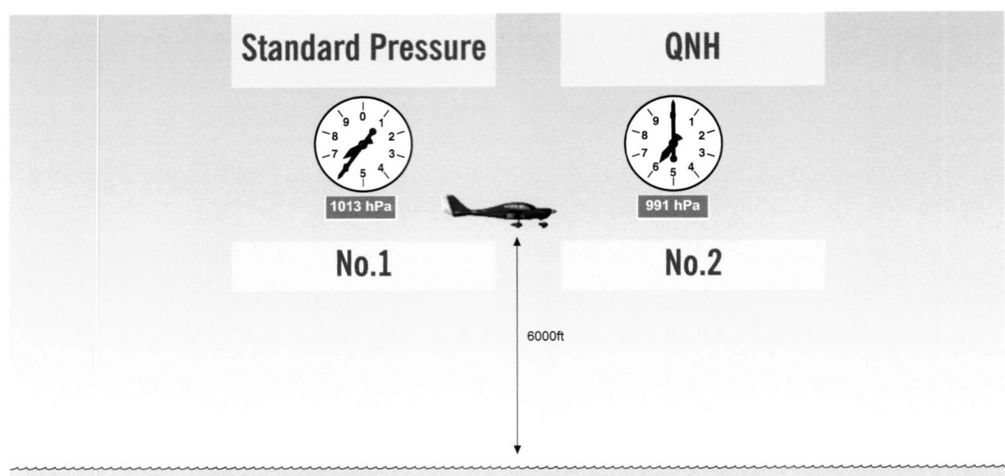

Figure AL6.16
If the QNH is 991 hPa, at altitude 6000ft (amsl) the aircraft is at flight level (FL)66.

Imagine a day when the QNH is 991hPa, and assume that the aircraft has two altimeters. As the aircraft reaches the Transition Altitude, which we will assume is 6000ft, No. 1 altimeter is reset from 991hPa to the standard pressure of 1013hPa. If the aircraft was flown level at this point, the No. 1 altimeter now reads 6660ft, the No. 2 altimeter still set to QNH still reads 6000 feet. The difference between the two altimeter readings of 660ft is the difference in hectopascals multiplied by the average feet per hectopascal (if 1hPa is equivalent to 30ft, 22hPa x 30 feet = 660 feet). But remember, the aircraft is still at 6000ft altitude above mean sea level. Only the No. 1 altimeter setting (and hence the No. 1 altimeter reading) has changed.

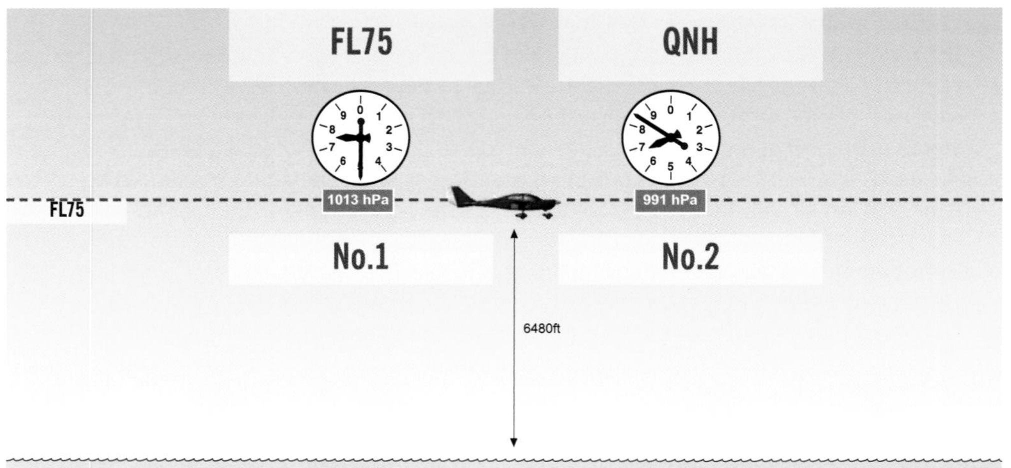

Figure AL6.17
If the QNH is 991 hPa, at flight level (FL) 75 the aircraft is at altitude 6480ft (amsl).

Now, let us further assume that the aircraft has a cruising magnetic track of between 000 and 179 degrees, which (when above the Transition Altitude) dictates a VFR cruising Flight Level of odd Flight Levels + 500ft. If the pilot has decided to fly at FL75, the aircraft can climb until the No.1 altimeter (set to 1013hPa) reads 7500ft. At this point, the aircraft is flying at FL75, and at the same time its altitude (above mean sea level) is 660ft lower – ie 6840ft. This altitude will be displayed on the no.2 altimeter which is still set to QNH.

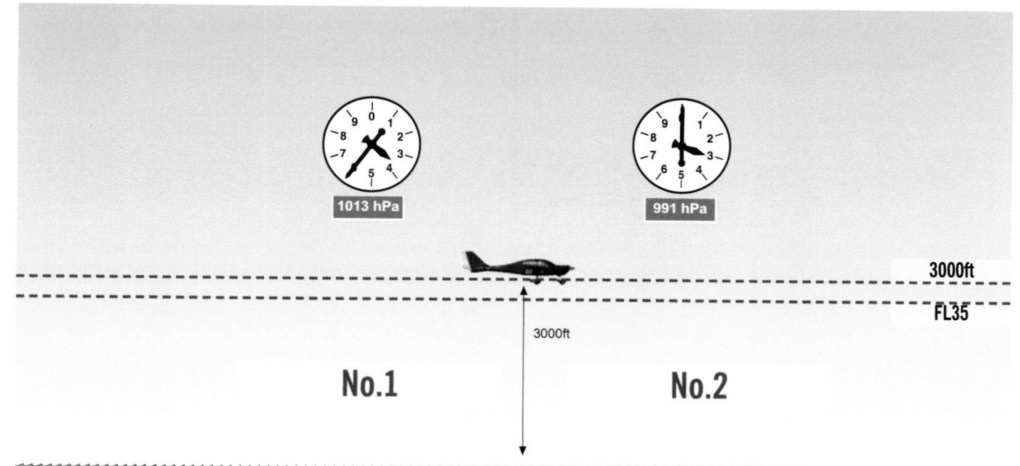

Figure AL6.18
Aircraft can only use Flight Levels which are above the transition altitude. In this case (when the QNH is 991 hPa), FL35 is below a transition altitude of 3000ft and so is unusable on this day.

Taking this example one stage further, using the same QNH of 991hPa, imagine that the Transition Altitude is 3000ft and the desired flight level is FL35 (that is, 3,500 feet indicated with the standard pressure set on the altimeter). When the aircraft reaches 3000ft altitude and the pilot sets the standard setting on the no1 altimeter, the aircraft is already at 3660ft on the standard pressure setting (that is FL36). To reach FL35 the aircraft would need to descend below the Transition Altitude.

This is not permitted, because flight levels always start *above* the Transition Altitude.

Therefore on this day, with this QNH, FL35 is not available. The first available VFR flight level on this magnetic track will be will be FL55, at which level the aircraft altitude (amsl) will be 4840 feet, that is FL55 – 660 feet.

A VFR flight cruising in level flight above the Transition Altitude should fly at the appropriate flight level unless ATC require or allow otherwise.

Of course, it may not be possible to operate on the appropriate VFR cruising flight level and remain clear of controlled airspace (for example, a Class A airway). On an aeronautical chart, the base of controlled airspace will be stated when it is above the surface. The base of controlled airspace may be defined as an altitude (and so referenced to QNH), although controlled airspace with a base above the transition altitude is more likely to have a base defined as a Flight Level, abbreviated on an aeronautical chart to 'FL'. As a general rule, when flying below controlled airspace the QNH of any airfield beneath that controlled airspace can be used as the altimeter setting.

In some states, the base of controlled or notified airspace in mountainous areas may be defined as a level above the surface – sometimes abbreviated to 'ASFC' (Above SurFaCe).

Figure AL6.19
This VFR aeronautical chart shows class A controlled airspace (Worthing CTA) with a base of FL75 south of the boundary; north of the boundary line the London TMA (LTMA) has a base of 5500ft amsl.

EGTK AD 2.17 AIR TRAFFIC SERVICES AIRSPACE

Designation and lateral limits	Vertical Limits	Airspace Class	ATS unit callsign/ language	Transition Altitude	Remarks
1	2	3	4	5	6
OXFORD/KIDLINGTON AERO-DROME TRAFFIC ZONE (ATZ) A circle, 2 nm radius centred at 515013N 0011912W on longest notified runway (01/19)	Upper limit: 2000 ft Lower limit: SFC	G	OXFORD APPROACH English	6000 ft	

Figure AL6.20
The AIP entry for Oxford in the UK shows that the Transition Altitude at Oxford is 6000ft.

The Transition Altitude is NOT common across European airspace, it varies between different states, and may vary at different airfields and vary in and below different areas of controlled airspace. The actual Transition Level for an airfield or an area of airspace will be found in the relevant AIP and can also be advised by ATC.

When descending from cruising flight at a flight level, QNH can be used once cleared to an altitude or once below the Transition Level. The VFR pilot has the choice of whether to use QNH or QFE for landing – the trend is towards using QNH for approach and landing, in which case it is particularly important to know the airfield elevation in order to join the circuit or approach at the correct altitude and integrate with the existing traffic pattern. If an aircraft makes a 'missed approach' (that is, climbs away from an approach without landing) at a controlled aerodrome, ATC will almost certainly give instructions in relation to airfield QNH and expect level reports to be made in terms of altitude.

Progress Check

57. What does an altimeter measure?
58. What is the correct aeronautical term if an aircraft is flying by reference to vertical distance 'above mean sea level' (amsl)?
59. If an aircraft flies from an area of high pressure to an area of low pressure without re-setting the altimeter sub-scale, but at a constant indicated level, what is likely to happen?
60. If an altimeter is set to the 'QFE' pressure setting, what is the reference it is using and what is the correct term for the vertical distance displayed on the altimeter?
61. An aircraft is on the surface of an airfield with an elevation of 330ft, the airfield QFE is 1003hPa. Assuming 1 hPa = 30ft, what should the pilot expect the airfield QNH to be?
62. When in cruising flight 'en-route', on a VFR flight below the Transition Altitude and below a Control Area, what altimeter setting would normally be used?
63. What is the 'Transition Level'?
64. What is the Standard Pressure altimeter setting in hPa?
65. If QNH is 1003hPa and the aircraft is at FL55, what is the aircraft's altitude?
66. An aircraft is in level cruising VFR flight on a magnetic track of 270°M, the QNH is 995hpa and the Transitional Altitude is 5000ft. What is the lowest available Flight Level to comply with VFR?

These questions are intended to test knowledge and reinforce some of the key learning points from this section. In answering these questions, a 'pass rate' of around 80% should be the target.

Model answers are found at page 146

Intentionally Left Blank

AL7 Air Traffic Services

Air Traffic Control Service

Flight Information Service

Alerting Service

AL7 Air Traffic Services

Air Traffic Control Service

There is a popular misunderstanding amongst non-pilots that all flights (crewed by steely-eyed pilots with gold bars and aviator sunglasses, of course) are subject to clearances from a grey-haired air traffic controller (sitting at the top of a control tower and armed with a radar screen and a pair of binoculars. And always drinking from a plastic coffee cup). The truth, of course, is rather less romantic and significantly more complex. This is particularly true for VFR flights which in many circumstances can operate without requiring any sort of clearance and without needing to talk to anyone on the ground, Air Traffic Controller or otherwise.

There is also a common misconception amongst student pilots that Air Traffic Controllers are a frightening species, completely unforgiving of errors or omissions by pilots and just waiting for the chance to punish the unwary aviator. Again, the truth is rather different, but it is fair to say that relations between those flying aircraft and those talking to them are much better if both parties understand the appropriate procedures and operate to the same rules. Unfortunately, too many VFR pilots find it easier to avoid contact with Air Traffic Controllers wherever possible and so miss out on assistance and support that can actually ease a pilot's workload and make VFR flight a safer and more efficient means of transport.

Figure AL7.1
OK – they often have binoculars and drink coffee.

One of the first points to understand is that not every person who answers a radio call from the pilot is an air traffic controller providing an Air Traffic Control Service, and even when the pilot is in communication with an ATC unit, that unit may not be in a position to provide 'clearances' or instructions. It is one of the features of VFR flight, especially outside controlled airspace and away from a controlled aerodrome, that there may be only a limited scope for an ATC unit to provide a 'control' service. Indeed many of the people talking to VFR flights may not be qualified or equipped to offer any sort of clearance or instructions at all.

To understand more, a few definitions are required:

Air Traffic Service (ATS)	A general term meaning the provision of a control, information, advisory, or alerting, service to flights.
Air Traffic Service Unit (ATSU)	A location providing some form of Air Traffic Service.
Air Traffic Control Service	A service provided to prevent collisions and maintain an orderly flow of air traffic.

Figure AL7.2
Air traffic service definitions.

In practical terms, an **Air Traffic Control Service** can only be provided by an Air Traffic Controller operating from a location that is properly equipped and approved. Controllers have training, licensing and currency requirements just as pilots do and they can only provide a control service if they have specified equipment and approvals and operate in accordance with defined rules and procedures.

Figure AL7.3
An Air Traffic Control Service can only be provided by an Air Traffic Controller operating at an approved location.

At an airfield which has an ATC service (that is, a 'controlled' aerodrome), all aerodrome traffic is subject to an aerodrome control service from the control tower. In practice this means that a departing VFR flight has to make contact on the appropriate radio frequency to request taxiing permission before leaving the parking spot (although it is not normally necessary for a VFR flight to request clearance for engine start). In response to that initial call, the following information is normally given:

- Runway in use
- Surface wind direction and speed
- Aerodrome QNH

At larger aerodromes, an **Automatic Terminal Information Service** (**ATIS**) may be in use. ATIS is a recorded radio broadcast of airfield and meteorological information for departing and arriving flights, updated regularly. On first contact with an aerodrome ATC unit the pilot should confirm that current ATIS broadcast has been received (so that the controller doesn't have to repeat all that information to the pilot).

Once the initial call from a departing flight has been made and two-way communication established, there are certain key points of traffic flow on and around a controlled aerodrome.

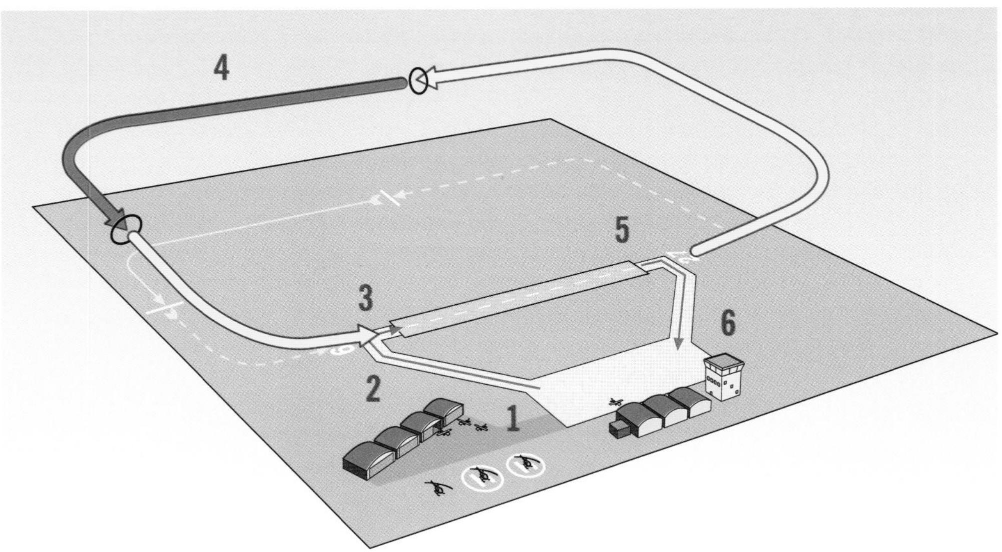

Figure AL7.4
The key points of traffic flow on and around a controlled aerodrome.
1 Initial call from a departing flight
2 Point of departing traffic to be held if there is conflicting traffic. This is also usually the point used for power and pre-take off checks
3 Take-off clearance issued here if not at position 2
4 Landing clearance issued
5 Clearance to taxi to parking area given
6 Parking information given if necessary

Before take-off, an aircraft will normally be advised of the surface wind and any significant weather conditions in the take-off and climb-out area. Additionally, at all times when a flight is in contact with an aerodrome ATC unit the pilot can expect to receive information on other local traffic, including any aircraft, vehicle or person on the manoeuvring area and any traffic operating in the vicinity of the aerodrome, which may be a hazard to the flight.

In the case of an arriving flight, before entering the traffic pattern at a controlled aerodrome, the pilot should be provided with the following information:

- Runway in use
- Surface wind direction and speed
- Aerodrome QNH (and aerodrome or runway QFE if appropriate)

Again, the pilot can also expect to be provided with traffic information and ATC will specify an order for landing (eg *"Cleared to final No. 1"*, *"Cleared to Final No.2"* etc.). A VFR flight is expected to comply with this order of landing by maintaining its own separation from other traffic. This is a good place to repeat that a VFR flight, even within controlled airspace, is not necessarily automatically separated from other aircraft. It is more common that ATC will provide information on other traffic so that the flight can maintain its own separation. ATC may offer advice on avoiding other traffic if requested. It is also worth repeating that the pilot is assumed to be complying with ATC instructions unless otherwise stated. If a pilot is unable to comply with an instruction, or is forced to depart from an accepted clearance for safety reasons, ATC must be informed immediately.

Every ATS unit is allocated a 'call sign' which is used in radio communications and notified in the AIP. This call sign indicates to the pilot not just the location of the ATSU but also the type of service being provided. An aerodrome control service will take the name of the airfield followed by a word describing the type of ATC service being provided, for example:

[aerodrome name] *"Tower"* – sometimes abbreviated in aeronautical publications to 'TWR'.

[aerodrome name] *"Ground"* – sometimes abbreviated in aeronautical publications to 'GND'.

On initial contact with an ATS unit the pilot is expected to use the appropriate call sign, which the ATS unit will acknowledge (or correct, if necessary) so that there is no confusion about the type of service being provided to the flight.

An airfield within controlled airspace, or with regular IFR traffic, is likely to provide an **approach control service** – an ATC service for arriving and departing 'controlled flights'. A **controlled flight** is any flight subject to an ATC clearance. An approach control service is also likely to be the service used by aircraft transiting (passing through) controlled airspace around an airfield.

An aircraft departing a controlled aerodrome may be transferred to the approach control service until clear of the airfield and any controlled airspace around it. An aircraft arriving at a controlled aerodrome will usually be expected to make initial contact with the approach control service where it exists. If the airfield has an ATIS broadcast, this should be checked by an arriving flight before contacting the approach controller and receipt of the current information confirmed in the initial call.

As with other ATC services, the contact frequencies, call signs and hours of operation of an approach control service will be found in the AIP. The correct call signs should be used on initial contact with any ATC unit and will be confirmed (or corrected) by the controller. In addition to an approach control service, ATC services for airspace (and particularly controlled airspace) around an airfield may have a number of different call signs, usually prefixed with the airfield name (or the name of the airfield responsible for an area of controlled airspace), for example:

[name] *"Approach"* – sometimes abbreviated in aeronautical publications to 'APP'

[name] *"Radar"* – sometimes abbreviated in aeronautical publications to 'RAD'

[name] *"Director"*

[name] *"Zone"*

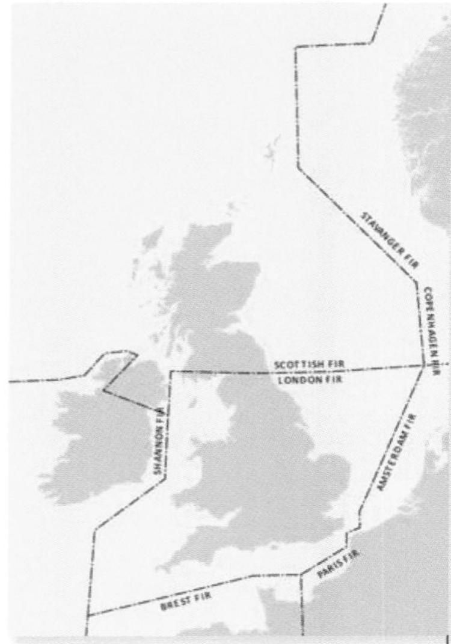

Figure AL7.5
Flight Information Regions.

Figure AL7.6
An FIR boundary as depicted on an aeronautical chart.

Flight Information Service

A **Flight Information Service** provides *"...advice and information useful for the safe and efficient conduct of flights."* A Flight Information Service (FIS) differs to an ATC service in that, except in very specific circumstances, a Flight Information Service cannot give instructions or clearances to flights. A Flight Information Service is normally available at a specific airfield, or to cover a large geographical area.

The region within which a state will provide a flight information service is called (unsurprisingly) the **Flight Information Region** (**FIR**). These regions will usually cover all of a state's territory, from the surface to an upper limit specified in the AIP, but typically around Flight Level 195 (that is, 19,500 feet above the 1013hPa pressure datum). FIR boundaries are marked on aeronautical charts. Above European FIRs there is an Upper Information Region (UIR), which may have different boundaries to the FIRs.

A larger state may have a number of FIRs, each defined by a very approximate geographic area – for example London FIR, Paris FIR, Madrid FIR etc. Within a FIR a Flight Information Service will be provided, primarily for use by aircraft flying outside controlled airspace and not in contact with any other ATS unit.

The Flight Information Service provided within a FIR is intended primarily to provide information on matters such as known navigation hazards, serviceability of navigation aids and weather conditions at airfields. So, for example, a pilot might contact a FIS provider to request the present weather at the destination airfield while 'en-route' to that airfield. The FIS unit may also be able to act as a liaison to contact or co-ordinate with another ATS units and contact with an FIS unit may be required for a VFR flight crossing an international boundary. The FIS unit will also provide information on any known collision hazards or conflicting traffic, but this information is likely to be very limited. Only a very small number of aircraft in a FIR will be in contact with any particular FIS unit and that unit may not have radar or other means of monitoring traffic not on the same radio frequency. In a large FIR, it is common for different radio frequencies to be in use in different sectors of the FIR, and these will be marked on aeronautical charts. Full details of FIS frequencies (including hours of operation and coverage) will also be found in the AIP.

Figure AL7.7
Inside a typical AFIS unit.

A FIS unit covering a FIR or a region within a FIR will often have access to very good resources to provide information to pilots and assistance where necessary. However, the service a FIS unit can offer may be limited, in particular by the number of other aircraft also on the same frequency at the same time and possibly also requesting information or assistance. There are certain FIS frequencies within Europe which can get very busy at times, during which complicated or detailed conversations may not be feasible.

A Flight Information Service provided at a specific airfield within Europe may be provided by an **Aerodrome Flight Information Service** unit, and such a service may be referred to as an 'AFIS'. An AFIS provides a flight information service to aerodrome traffic at and in the vicinity of a specific airfield. In practice this means that the pilot can expect to receive information on runway in use, weather conditions, local traffic, known hazards etc.

The procedures for contacting an AFIS unit are similar to those for an aerodrome control service, the principal difference is that the service being provided is one of information, rather than control. In some states, an AFIS unit may provide instructions in very specific circumstances, but these are a matter of national procedure rather than international agreement and in general the pilot should not expect a control service.

An aerodrome FIS may be provided at an airfield where the amount or type of traffic does not justify a full aerodrome control service, or may be provided during certain hours or days at an airfield which has a control service at other times. Full details of an AFIS will be found in the appropriate aerodrome entry in the AIP.

A unit providing a Flight Information Service within a FIR will use a call sign which consists of the FIR or region and the word 'information', for example:

'Scottish Information'	provides a FIS in the Scottish FIR
'Lyon Information'	provides a FIS service in the Lyon region of the Marseille FIR

At an airfield providing an AFIS, the call sign will be the airfield name followed by the word "*Information*" or "*AFIS*" depending on the state, for example:

'Fairoaks Information'	provides an AFIS service at Fairoaks airfield (UK)
'Stauning AFIS'	provides an AFIS service at Stauning airfield (Denmark)

Alerting Service

An **alerting service** will notify the appropriate organisations if an aircraft requires Search and Rescue (SAR) assistance.

Whenever a flight is receiving an air traffic control service, or a flight information service, it is also by default receiving an alerting service. An alerting service is not a 'stand alone' option, but means that when a flight is known to the air traffic services, if it declares an emergency, or goes missing, the appropriate agencies will be informed and action taken to locate the aircraft and provide assistance.

The alerting service is a very good reason for maintaining contact with an ATS unit even when the flight does not require a control or information service. Even in parts of Europe considered to be densely inhabited, there have been plenty of instances of aircraft making unplanned landings and not being located for some time, if no-one is initially aware that they have gone missing. In the more sparsely populated areas of Europe and in areas particularly difficult for Search and Rescue – such as mountains and the sea – locating a downed aircraft and its occupants can take much longer. The purpose of an alerting service is that there should not be any undue delay in starting SAR operations.

This advantage of being in contact with an ATS unit is one of the reasons that a prudent pilot will often establish two-way communications with an ATS unit, especially if flying over a remote area, even when there is no specific requirement or other reason to do so. In effect, the pilot is taking advantage of the (free) service which can mobilise very significant rescue services if the need arises.

This service does come with an obligation however, which is that the pilot must inform the ATS unit before leaving the frequency. If a flight simply 'disappears' from a radio frequency, the ATS unit has no way of knowing if the pilot is merely inconsiderate, or has a problem. At best, the ATS unit may waste some time contacting other ATS units and agencies to see if the flight has transferred to them. At worst, a totally unnecessary (and very expensive) SAR operation may be launched. Neither of these options are going to make the pilot popular or be helpful to the Air Traffic and SAR services, so do remember to say goodbye before leaving a radio frequency.

Figure AL7.8
When flying over remote or sparsely populated areas, it is good practice to maintain contact with an ATC or FIS unit in order to receive an alerting service.

Progress Check

67. What is a 'controlled' aerodrome?
68. What is ATIS?
69. What is an 'approach control service'?
70. Where can information be found on ATC services – including call sign, contact frequency, hours of operation etc?
71. What is a service which provides *"...advice and information useful for the safe and efficient conduct of flights."*?
72. What is a FIR?
73. What service does an AFIS provide?
74. In what circumstances is a flight receiving an 'alerting service'?

These questions are intended to test knowledge and reinforce some of the key learning points from this section. In answering these questions, a 'pass rate' of around 80% should be the target.

Model answers are found at page 146

AL8 Aeronautical Information Service (AIS)

Aeronautical Information Service (AIS)

Aeronautical Information Publication (AIP)

NOTAMs

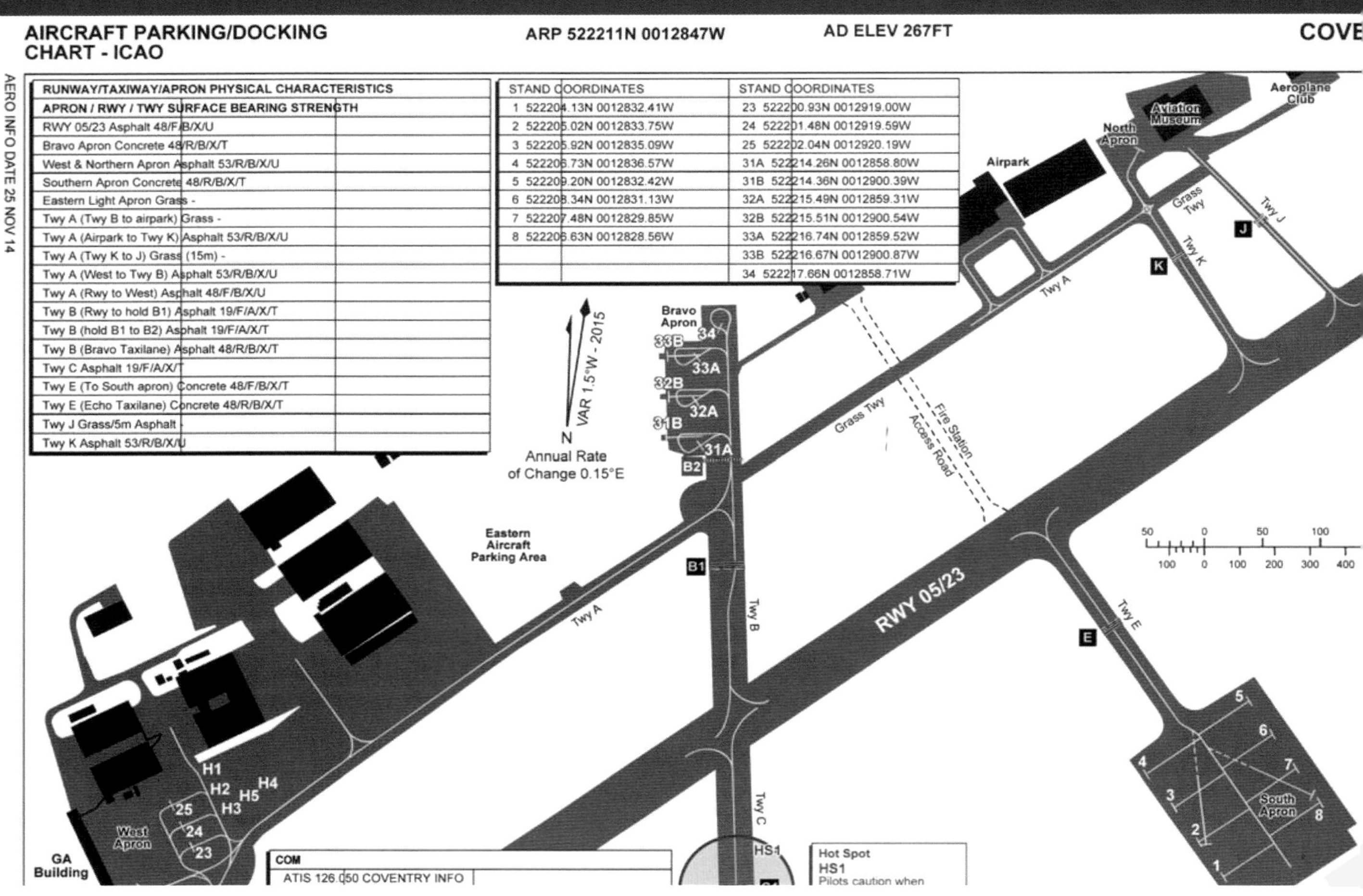

RUNWAY/TAXIWAY/APRON PHYSICAL CHARACTERISTICS
APRON / RWY / TWY SURFACE BEARING STRENGTH
RWY 05/23 Asphalt 48/F/B/X/U
Bravo Apron Concrete 48/R/B/X/T
West & Northern Apron Asphalt 53/R/B/X/U
Southern Apron Concrete 48/R/B/X/T
Eastern Light Apron Grass -
Twy A (Twy B to airpark) Grass -
Twy A (Airpark to Twy K) Asphalt 53/R/B/X/U
Twy A (Twy K to J) Grass (15m) -
Twy A (West to Twy B) Asphalt 53/R/B/X/U
Twy A (Rwy to West) Asphalt 48/F/B/X/U
Twy B (Rwy to hold B1) Asphalt 19/F/A/X/T
Twy B (hold B1 to B2) Asphalt 19/F/A/X/T
Twy B (Bravo Taxilane) Asphalt 48/R/B/X/T
Twy C Asphalt 19/F/A/X/T
Twy E (To South apron) Concrete 48/F/B/X/T
Twy E (Echo Taxilane) Concrete 48/R/B/X/T
Twy J Grass/5m Asphalt -
Twy K Asphalt 53/R/B/X/U

STAND	COORDINATES	STAND	COORDINATES
1	522204.13N 0012832.41W	23	522200.93N 0012919.00W
2	522205.02N 0012833.75W	24	522201.48N 0012919.59W
3	522205.92N 0012835.09W	25	522202.04N 0012920.19W
4	522206.73N 0012836.57W	31A	522214.26N 0012858.80W
5	522209.20N 0012832.42W	31B	522214.36N 0012900.39W
6	522208.34N 0012831.13W	32A	522215.49N 0012859.31W
7	522207.48N 0012829.85W	32B	522215.51N 0012900.54W
8	522206.63N 0012828.56W	33A	522216.74N 0012859.52W
		33B	522216.67N 0012900.87W
		34	522217.66N 0012858.71W

AL8 Aeronautical Information Service (AIS)

Aeronautical Information Service (AIS)

Each state will have some form of **Aeronautical Information Service** (**AIS**) which collects and distributes aeronautical data within a defined area of coverage. The AIS is responsible not only for collecting and publishing aeronautical information, but also for establishing a system to share this information within its own area and with other states. It is a feature of aeronautical information that it changes regularly, and those changes can have a profound effect on flight safety. It follows that the AIS must also have a system for distributing updates and amendments to aeronautical information as quickly and efficiently as possible.

As you might expect, virtually all AIS information and data is available via websites, with hard copy sources such as printed pages or CD-ROMs becoming less and less common. However, as with many other aspects of using the internet and the World Wide Web, it is vital to make sure that any aeronautical information sourced on-line is up-to-date and reliable. It is not uncommon for search engines to favour old information which has been extensively indexed, rather than newer information. Out-of-date aeronautical information may linger on the internet for many years and be referred to or linked from other documents or web pages. Virtually every state's AIS has an official website and it should normally be obvious that the correct information source has been reached (although, because they are heavily data-driven, few official AIS websites are likely to win many design awards!)

In terms of checking aeronautical information before flight, the emphasis is on the principle of 'self-briefing', in other words the pilot is expected to collate and check all the information necessary to make sure the flight can be completed safely. In theory, an airfield may provide briefing facilities where the pilot can access AIS documents. In practice, where this facility does exist it is most likely that AIS documents and information will be available via an internet-connected computer with limited 'hard copy' resources. Moreover, at many airfields, the pilot may need to rely on their own internet-capable devices to check AIS information. Checking such data on the average mobile phone can be a frustrating and tiresome business, so it makes sense to invest in a suitable device (such as a 'tablet'-sized pc or similar) with multiple internet connection options and a screen big enough to be able to read the data accessed. Although a state's aeronautical information is normally collated and distributed from a known location, it is rare that this location, or a briefing facility at an airfield, can offer anything approaching a personal pre-flight briefing service.

Figure AL8.1
AIS data is most often accessed via the relevant AIS provider's website – in this case the Belgian AIS.

Figure AL8.2
A 'self-briefing unit' at an airfield.

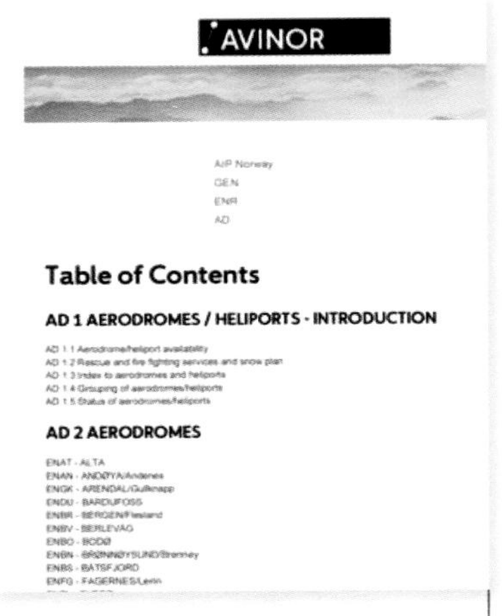

AVINOR

Table of Contents

AD 1 AERODROMES / HELIPORTS - INTRODUCTION

AD 2 AERODROMES

Figure AL8.3
A 'contents' page from the Norway AIP, listing the airfields for which AIP information is available.

There is one further caution. The AIS will normally be very good at collecting 'official' aeronautical data concerning airspace, navigation hazards and airfields which are in some way certified, regulated or licenced by the Competent Authority. However airfields and landing sites which fall outside this definition (such as private landing sites and helipads, sporting aviation sites, military airfields and sites used seasonally or temporarily) may not feature in the AIS system. For example, the UK has well over 1000 sites with some form of flying activity, but the UK AIS publishes detailed information for less than 120 airfields.

Aeronautical Information Publication (AIP)

The vast majority of the aeronautical data and information collected by an AIS is published in a document known as the **Aeronautical Information Publication** (**AIP**). By international agreement the AIP has a standard format (set-out in ICAO Annex 15) and most AIPs follow this standardised format closely. This makes it comparatively easy to find information in almost any state's AIP, once reasonably familiar the standard AIP structure.

The AIP is divided into three sections:

- GENERAL (GEN)
- EN-ROUTE (ENR)
- AERODROMES (AD)

Undoubtedly, the best way to become familiar with the AIP is to access and use it, so the following is not a list to be learnt but a guide to some of the information that is found in each AIP section:

GENERAL (GEN) Designated authorities, national regulation and differences to ICAO procedures, AIS abbreviations, sunrise/sunset tables, charts, air traffic services, meteorological services, search and rescue.

EN-ROUTE (ENR) Rules and procedures, airspace, navigation aids, prohibited restricted and danger areas, other navigation hazards, obstacles.

AERODROMES (AD) General aerodrome information, detailed information for individual aerodromes including airfield data, airspace, ATS units, communications, procedures and aerodrome charts.

Figure AL8.4
A sample 'AIRAC', giving advance notice of changes to the UK AIP, with replacement pages.

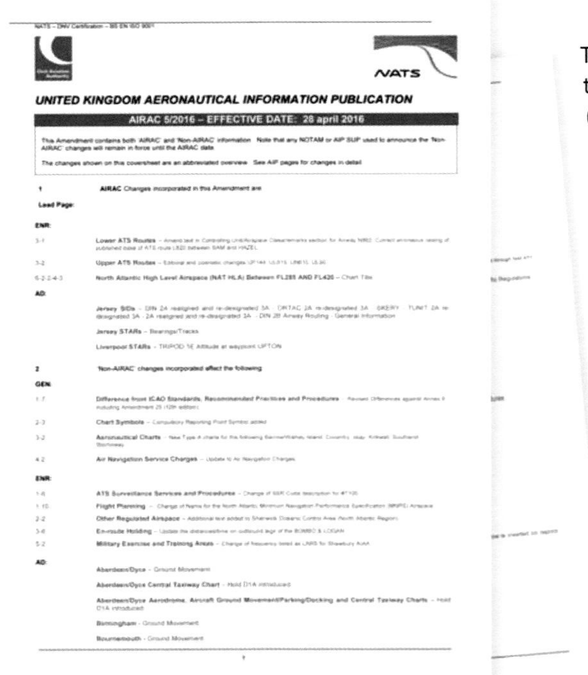

NATS

UNITED KINGDOM AERONAUTICAL INFORMATION PUBLICATION

AIRAC 5/2016 – EFFECTIVE DATE: 28 april 2016

The AIP is kept up-to-date largely through issuing replacement pages and these are mostly distributed through a system called **AIRAC** (**A**eronautical **I**nformation **R**egulation **A**nd **C**ontrol), which is a regular cycle for providing advance notification of permanent and operationally significant changes to the AIP. AIRAC provides up to eight weeks advance notice of such changes, and the AIRAC schedule is agreed world-wide. Because the AIRAC cycle operates in advance of changes, any information distributed through AIRAC will carry an 'effective date' – the date when the changes will come into force (for reasons that no-one can now remember, the effective date is always a Thursday). Replacement AIP pages issued through the AIRAC system will clearly indicate their effective date. Some minor amendments or those which have been pre-notified outside the AIRAC system may also be distributed through the AIRAC system but can be inserted on receipt – again the 'effective' date is printed on each individual page.

Changes to the AIP of a temporary nature – such as military exercises or work programs at an airfield – can be notified in the form of an **AIP Supplement** (sometimes abbreviated to **AIP SUP**). A supplement remains in the AIP for as long as all or some of the information within it remains valid.

The AIS may also publish information in the form of **Aeronautical Information Circulars** (AIC). An AIC contains information which does not qualify for inclusion within the AIP but may, for example, give notice of impending operational changes or add explanations or emphasis to matters of safety, operational significance, administration or regulation.

The complete suite of aeronautical data and information, including the AIP and its amendments and supplements, AICs and NOTAMs (described shortly) is sometimes called the 'Integrated Aeronautical Information Package'.

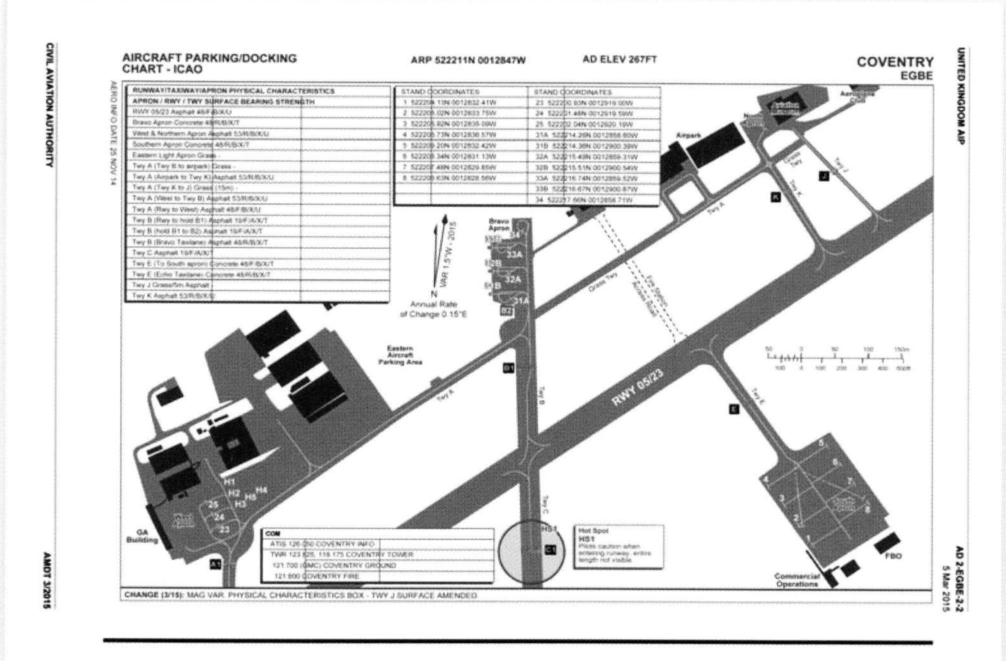

Figure AL8.5
A sample AIP supplement (AIP SUP) page.

Figure AL8.6
An Aeronautical Information Circular (AIC) giving safety information in relation to Wake Turbulence.

NOTAMs

The term **NOTAM** is believed to have been condensed from the phrase '**Not**ice to **A**ir **M**en' which gives some idea of how long this form of aeronautical information has been around. A NOTAM contains information or warnings which are too temporary, or too urgent, for inclusion within the normal system of updating and amending the AIP. According to ICAO, a NOTAM is a notice "*...concerning the establishment, condition or change in any aeronautical facility, service, procedure or hazard, the timely knowledge of which is essential to personnel concerned with flight operations.*"

As with other aeronautical information, NOTAMs are published in an internationally agreed format which is designed to make them easy to integrate into computerised flight planning and aeronautical information systems. Unfortunately, this means that a 'raw data' NOTAM looks less than user-friendly, although with a little explanation the key elements become clearer.

An ICAO-format NOTAM is divided into 'lines' each denoted by a letter. These lines have the following functions:

Figure AL8.7
The decoded lines of the standard NOTAM format

'Q' line	contains a heavily coded reference for the NOTAM, mostly of interest to the AIS itself, although the first letter group is the Flight Information Region affected by the NOTAM, and the last letter/number group is the position (in latitude and longitude) of the position the NOTAM relates to.
'A' line	the four letter ICAO code for the FIR or airfield affected by the NOTAM. For example, 'EHAA' is the ICAO code for Amsterdam FIR, 'EGLL' is the ICAO code for London Heathrow airport.
'B' line	the start date and time of the NOTAM, in the unusual format Year/Month/Date (YY/MM/DD) followed by the time in hours and minutes (hh/mm). In common with all other aeronautical information and data, time is given in terms of **Co-ordinated Universal Time (UTC)**, the term which replaced 'Greenwich Mean Time' (GMT) as the globally recognised time reference.
'C' line	the finish date and time, in the same unusual format as the 'B' line.
'D' line	where used, this indicates the daily hours of the NOTAM, if not 24 hours.
'E' line	a 'plain language' description of the NOTAM, although often making heavy use of aeronautical abbreviations.
'F' and 'G' lines	when used, show the vertical limits of the NOTAM.

Depending on how the NOTAM is presented, the 'Q', 'A', 'F' and 'G' lines may not be shown, although the 'B', 'C' and 'E' lines should always be available to be read.

Here is a sample NOTAM for the Scottish airfield of EDAY:

Figure AL8.8
A sample NOTAM – note the time and date groups – B) and C)

EDAY
Q) EGPX/QMRLC/IV/NBO/A/000/999/5911N00246W005
B) FROM: 16/03/11 17:00 **C)** TO: 16/06/11 18:00
E) RUNWAY 18/36 CLOSED DUE WATER LOGGING

This NOTAM covers the period from 17:00 UTC on 11th March 2016 to 18:00 UTC on 11th June 2016, and gives notice that runway 18/36 is closed due to waterlogging.

Here is another sample NOTAM:

ALADIN
Q) LFFF/QCTAS/I/B/AE/000/999/4838N00454E005
A) LFSI **B)** FROM: 16/05/07 06:00 **C)** TO: 16/05/07 11:00
E) ALADIN RADAR U/S. MAINTENANCE

Figure AL8.9
Another sample NOTAM – note the use of the abbreviation 'U/S' – unserviceable.

This NOTAM covers St Dizier airport in France (ICAO identifier LFSI), from 06:00 UTC on 7th May 2016 to 11:00 UTC on 7th May 2016, Aladin Radar unserviceable (U/S) [due to] maintenance.

It should be clear that the pilot in command has a responsibility to check NOTAMs before flight for information or warnings that may affect the route planned and airfields to be used. The exact presentation of NOTAMs, and methods for obtaining NOTAMs, varies between different AIS providers. As you might expect, virtually every AIS in the world has a website from which NOTAMs can be accessed, and as a general rule any AIS provider can access aeronautical data and NOTAMs from other AIS providers. In common with many other aspects of flight planning, internet access – whilst not mandatory – makes the pilot's task much, much easier.

At any one time there are likely to be hundreds of NOTAMs within a FIR, so some method has to be found to filter these down when checking for NOTAMs relevant to a planned flight. One method is for an AIS provider to group NOTAMs together, usually by area or region, in a document called a **Pre-flight Information Bulletin** (**PIB**). A PIB may cover a particular airfield (or group of airfields), an area or a specific route and as far as possible will be presented in plain language. Occasionally, the pilot may find printed PIBs in an airfield briefing office or flight planning area, but more commonly a PIB is accessed from the AIS provider via their website and, depending on the AIS provider, the pilot may be able to specify an exact route and receive a PIB containing only NOTAMs relevant to that route.

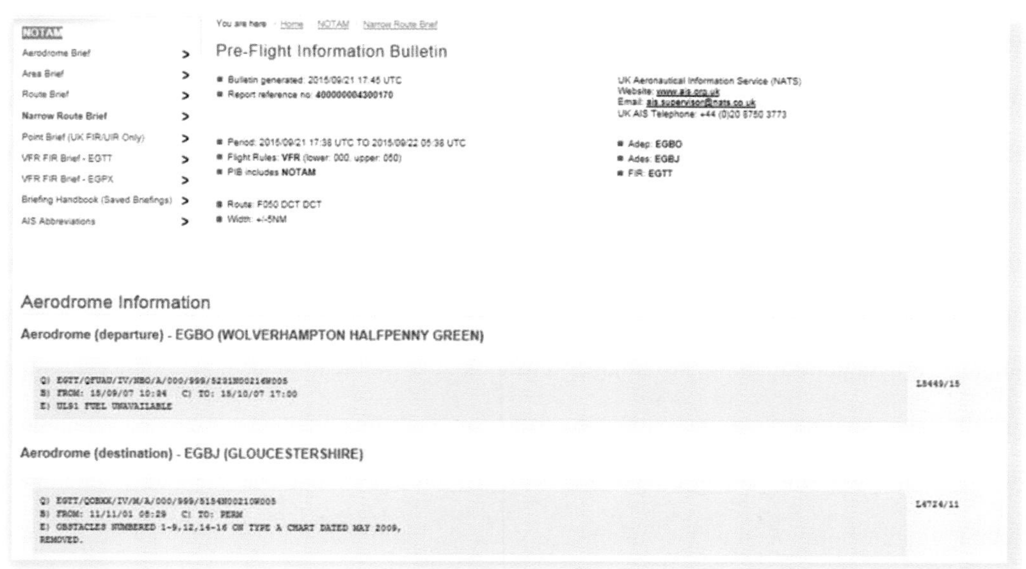

Figure AL8.10
A sample Pre-flight Information Bulletin (PIB).

There are also a number of commercially-produced flight planning applications (software) which will show NOTAMs both in list and graphic form, based on a specified route or area.

Whatever method is used for accessing and checking NOTAMs, the most important action is simply that of checking NOTAMs before flight. There are few things more depressing to witness in aviation than a pilot blundering into an active air display, for example, simply because he or she hadn't bothered to check the NOTAMs before flight. This is not only highly dangerous but, in some circumstances, may lead to the pilot being prosecuted for endangering the safety of their flight and the safety other aircraft and pilots (and possibly even spectators on the ground).

Progress Check

75 In what section of the AIP would you expect to find information on specific airfields?

76 What does AIRAC provide?

77 What is a NOTAM?

78 What is the correct decode of the following dates and times as featured in a NOTAM?
B) FROM: 16/04/05 11:07 C) TO: 16/07/04 23:59

79 What is the correct decode of the following NOTAM text?
CARLISLE ATZ DEACTIVATED. ATS NOT AVBL. AD NOT AVBL TO ACFT EXCEPT
WITH OUT OF HOURS PERMISSION.

These questions are intended to test knowledge and reinforce some of the key learning points from this section. In answering these questions, a 'pass rate' of around 80% should be the target.

Model answers are found at page 147

Intentionally Left Blank

AL9 Urgency and Distress Procedures

Urgency situation

Distress situation

Interception of civil aircraft

AL9 Urgency and Distress Procedures

Urgency situation

The rules of the air, and various other aspects of aviation law and procedures, allow an aircraft with an emergency to take priority over all other aircraft and to disregard ATC instructions if necessary.

Neither ICAO nor EASA give a formal definition of what constitutes an emergency; maybe the implication is that this is a matter for pilot judgement rather than dry legal designation.

Figure AL9.1
It is up to the pilot alone to decide what constitutes an emergency and how serious that emergency is. Once a pilot has 'declared' an emergency, all other agencies (ATC etc) are required to give any assistance the pilot requires.

Nevertheless, although there is no formal definition of what constitutes an 'emergency' in aviation, and any emergency is likely to be a non-standard situation, two levels of emergency are generally recognised.

An **urgency** situation can be defined as *"...a condition concerning the safety of an aircraft or other vehicle, or of some person on board or within sight, but one which does not require immediate assistance."* This can be considered as circumstances where some form of abnormal situation exists but there is no immediate danger to the aircraft or its occupants. Possible examples of an urgency situation (which should not be taken as absolute criteria nor a comprehensive list) include:

- An aircraft or equipment malfunction which requires a diversion and/or priority landing;
- The aircraft is lost but not in immediate danger;
- The weather situation means that the flight requires urgent assistance and/or priority handling by ATC;
- A passenger requires medical assistance;
- The flight crew is aware of another aircraft, vehicle or person with an emergency.

If a pilot is facing an emergency situation, it is important – where appropriate – to make others aware of it so that they can offer assistance, or at the very least stay out of the way! There are a number of signals which can be used to indicate that an aircraft has an urgency situation and a very urgent message to transmit regarding the safety of the aircraft or some other aircraft, vehicle or person:

- The spoken words *"Pan Pan, Pan Pan, Pan Pan"*
- The Morse code for the letters 'XXX' (— •• —   — •• —   — •• —)

Additionally, if a pilot wishes to give notice of difficulties which compel the aircraft to land, but do not require immediate assistance, they can make the following light signals:

- Repeatedly switching the landing light(s) on and off
- Repeated irregular switching of the navigation lights on and off

If a pilot is facing an urgency situation, there should be no hesitation in using one of these signals (in particular the spoken words 'Pan Pan') in order to get any assistance or priority handling which will ensure the safety of the aircraft or its occupants. SERA is quite clear that, *"In the case of an aircraft known or believed to be in a state of emergency...air traffic services units shall give the aircraft maximum consideration, assistance and priority over other aircraft as may be necessitated by the circumstances."* There is sometimes a reluctance by a pilot to declare an emergency situation or admit that there is a serious problem, which can lead to delays in receiving priority status or assistance because - as any air traffic controller will confirm - ATC skills do not include mind reading! In short, any pilot facing an emergency or abnormal situation must be prepared to say so, accept any assistance that will be useful, and remember that all emergency assistance is made available free of charge or consequences.

Figure AL9.2
Emergencies are, by their very nature, not standard and it is the pilot who decides what is the appropriate action to take.

An aircraft that has an urgency situation can expect to take priority over all other flights, except a flight which has a 'distress' situation.

Distress situation

A **distress** situation is *"...a condition of being threatened by serious and/or imminent danger and requiring immediate assistance."*

A distress situation is the highest level of emergency and a more serious condition than an urgency situation. So, any circumstance more serious than an 'urgency' situation is a 'distress' situation. Possible examples of a distress situation (which should not be taken as absolute criteria nor a comprehensive list) include:

- An aircraft or equipment malfunction which represents imminent danger to the aircraft occupants;
- The imminent danger of running out of fuel;
- A weather situation which threatens immediate danger to the aircraft and its occupants;
- An aircraft occupant requires immediate medical assistance.

Figure AL9.3
'Distress' – a condition of being threatened by serious and/or imminent danger and requiring immediate assistance.

A distress situation can be notified by the following signals:

- The spoken words *"Mayday, Mayday, Mayday"*
- The Morse code for the letters 'SOS' (••• — — — •••)
- Red signals or flares fired from the aircraft

Just as with an urgency situation, a pilot should not hesitate to declare a distress situation if the circumstances suggest it is an appropriate course of action. An aircraft in 'distress' will be given priority over all other flights.

It is worth knowing that not all states, especially those outside Europe, recognise an 'urgency' situation and in particular the spoken words *"Pan Pan"*. In circumstances where the pilot is having trouble communicating that an urgency situation exists, the safest course of action may be to declare a distress situation instead – in particular by using the spoken word *"Mayday"*, which is recognised globally as indicating a serious emergency.

Figure AL9.4
The aircraft's transponder can be used to indicate an emergency situation.

An emergency situation can also be indicated by using one of three internationally-recognised transponder codes. A **transponder** (sometimes abbreviated to **XPDR**) is a piece of aircraft equipment which transmits data to a ground station equipped with **Secondary Surveillance Radar** (**SSR**). In addition to the four number code selected by the pilot, a transponder may transmit other information including the aircraft's level and identification, and this information is displayed at the aircraft's position on a radar screen.

Transponder Code	Meaning	Notes
7700	To indicate an emergency situation	This code should be selected whenever the pilot has specific reason to believe that this is the best course of action (although having due regard for the over-riding importance of controlling aircraft and containing the emergency). If the aircraft is already transmitting a transponder code and receiving an air traffic service, that existing code may be retained at the discretion of either the pilot or the controller.
7600	To indicate a radio failure	
7500	To indicate unlawful interference	Meaning unlawful interference with the planned operation of a flight, this code is used unless circumstances dictate the use of 7700.

Figure AL9.5
The transponder emergency codes.

The use of one of the emergency transponder codes means that any suitably equipped radar unit within radar range of the aircraft will see the code, regardless of whether or not they are in radio contact with the aircraft. In that respect it's a very good way for drawing attention to yourself. However, as with all other emergency signals it's a matter of pilot judgement as to when, or if, to make use of these signals. In any emergency situation the pilot must make any number of decisions and take any number of actions to secure the safety of the flight, and it may be that these actions must take priority over communicating with the outside world. There is a well-known aviation adage that a pilot's priorities, in order of importance, must always be:

Aviate : Navigate: Communicate

This saying is never truer than in an emergency situation – getting involved in detailed discussions with ATC, for example, is a bad idea if it distracts the pilot from the primary task of flying the aircraft. Put another way, don't drop the aircraft in order to fly the microphone!

Interception of civil aircraft

The airborne interception of a civilian aircraft remains an unusual occurrence, although not a completely unknown event. There are no specific guidelines on what circumstances might trigger an interception, but the types of situation that can lead to an interception include:

- An aircraft has strayed from its expected route, or has entered danger, prohibited or restricted airspace, or otherwise is somewhere it shouldn't be;
- An aircraft has lost communications with ATC, or is unidentified;
- An aircraft is known, or believed, to be subject to, or at risk of, 'unlawful interference';
- An aircraft does not have the appropriate diplomatic clearances.

Figure AL9.6
This 'interception' was in fact a pre-arranged publicity photo opportunity.

The business of a military aircraft intercepting a civilian aircraft is not a routine matter, and it is essential that the pilots establish some form of communications as quickly as possible and follow agreed procedures.

The intercepted aircraft may not be aware of an impending interception until a military aircraft appears, slightly ahead of and above the intercepted aircraft, usually on the left-hand side. As initial actions, the intercepted aircraft should:

- Comply immediately with any instructions from the intercepting aircraft;
- If possible, notify the ATSU in communication with the flight;
- Attempt to establish contact with the intercepting aircraft on the international VHF emergency frequency of 121.5MHz, giving the identity of the intercepted aircraft and the nature of the flight;
- If equipped with a transponder, select the code 7700 unless otherwise instructed by the appropriate ATSU;
- If equipped with ADS-B or ADS-C, select the appropriate emergency functionality, if available, unless otherwise instructed by the appropriate ATSU.

The intercepting aircraft may use visual signals to give instructions to the intercepted aircraft. Those signals, and their meanings, are as below:

Figure AL9.7
The visual instructions an intercepting aircraft may give.

INTERCEPTING AIRCRAFT SIGNAL	MEANING	INTERCEPTED AIRCRAFT RESPONSE	MEANING
Takes up position, rocking aircraft and flashing lights irregularly. After acknowledgement makes slow level turn on to desired heading (Note 1.)	You have been intercepted, follow me	Rocks aircraft, flashes navigation lights at irregular intervals	Understood, will comply
Makes an abrupt breakaway manoeuvre, a climbing turn of 90° or more without crossing the flightpath of the intercepted aircraft	You may proceed	Rocks aircraft	Understood, will comply
Lowers undercarriage (if applicable), showing steady landing light and overflies runway or helicopter landing area	Land here	Lowers undercarriage if applicable, shows steady landing light, proceeds to land if safe	Understood, will comply
In the case of interception of a helicopter by a helicopter, makes a landing approach coming to hover near the landing area	Land here	As above	Understood, will comply

Note 1. If the intercepting aircraft is faster than the intercepted aircraft, it may fly a series of 'race-track' patterns and rock the aircraft each time it passes the intercepted aircraft.

The aircraft that has been intercepted may make signals to the interceptor, as below:

INTERCEPTED AIRCRAFT SIGNAL	MEANING	INTERCEPTING AIRCRAFT RESPONSE	MEANING
Raises undercarriage (if applicable) and flashes landing light(s) or other lights whilst passing over the runway between 1000ft and 2000ft AGL and continuing to circle the runway in use	The aerodrome you have designated is inadequate	Raises undercarriage and gives signal for the intercepted aircraft to follow	Understood, follow me
		or Raises undercarriage and makes breakaway manoeuvre	Understood, you may proceed
In the case of a helicopter, raises landing gear (if applicable) whilst between 170ft and 330ft AGL, continues to circle landing area, irregularly flashes available lights	The landing area you have designated is inadequate	As above	As above
Regular switching on and off of all available lights	Cannot Comply	Rocks aircraft	Understood
Irregular flashing of all available lights	In distress	Rocks aircraft	Understood

Figure AL9.8
The visual signals an intercepted aircraft may use.

Figure AL9.9
A practice interception carried out as part of a military exercise.

If radio contact is established during interception, but communication in a common language is not possible, the following phrases can be used, each transmitted twice:

Interceptor aircraft		
Phrase	**Pronunciation**	**Meaning**
CALL SIGN	**KOL** SA-IN	What is your call sign?
FOLLOW	**FOL**-LO	Follow me
DESCEND	DEE-**SEND**	Descend for landing
YOU LAND	**YOU LAAND**	Land at this aerodrome
PROCEED	PRO-**SEED**	You may proceed

Figure AL9.10
Radio phrases that may be used by an intercepting aircraft.

If any instructions received by radio conflict with those given by the intercepting aircraft by visual signals or radio, the intercepted aircraft should request immediate clarification while continuing to comply with the instructions given by the intercepting aircraft:

Intercepted aircraft		
Phrase	**Pronunciation**	**Meaning**
CALL SIGN	**KOL** SA-IN	My call sign is......
WILCO	**VILL**-KO	Understood, will comply
CAN NOT	**KANN**-NOT	Unable to comply
REPEAT	REE-**PEET**	Repeat your instruction
AM LOST	**AM LOSST**	Position unknown
MAYDAY	MAYDAY	I am in distress
HIJACK	**HI-JACK**	I have been hijacked
LAND	LAAND [place name]	I request landing at [place name]
DESCEND	DEE-SEND	I require descent

Figure AL9.11
Radio phrases that may be used by an intercepted aircraft.

Clearly the pilot of the intercepted aircraft must remain calm, be careful to acknowledge instructions and comply with them as far as possible. The use of hand signals is very specifically NOT recommended, as they can be misinterpreted!

In most states, practice interceptions of civilian aircraft are prohibited, unless very detailed prior arrangements and briefing has taken place. Therefore, an intercepted pilot should never assume that an interception is 'just a practice'.

Progress Check

80 What spoken word(s) indicate an 'urgency' situation?

81 What spoken word(s) indicate a 'distress' situation?

82 What light signals may a pilot use to indicate that the aircraft is compelled to land, but does not require immediate assistance?

83 What is the definition of a 'distress' situation?

84 What transponder code indicates an emergency situation?

85 What transponder code indicates a radio failure?

86 What radio frequency should be used to make contact with an intercepting aircraft?

87 What is the meaning of an intercepting aircraft rocking its wings, flashing its lights irregularly and slowly turning onto a new heading?

88 If instructions given by ATC conflict with instructions given by an intercepting aircraft, how should the intercepted aircraft respond?

These questions are intended to test knowledge and reinforce some of the key learning points from this section. In answering these questions, a 'pass rate' of around 80% should be the target.

Model answers are found at page 147

Intentionally Left Blank

AL10 Pilot Licensing

Medical certificates

Private Pilot Licence (PPL) privileges

Light Aircraft Pilot Licence (LAPL) privileges

Class Rating

Type Rating

Other Ratings and Certificates

AL10 Pilot Licensing

Medical certificates

In order to act as a pilot in command (and also as a 'co-pilot' where the aircraft type requires one) it is necessary to have undergone some form of aviation medical assessment. The details of that medical assessment (including its period of validity) will be recorded on the **medical certificate**. it is the pilot's responsibility to arrange a further assessment when necessary and act in accordance with any limitations specified on the medical certificate.

EASA recognises three types of aviation medical assessment:

- Class 1 Medical Certificate
- Class 2 Medical Certificate
- Light Aircraft Pilot Licence (LAPL) Medical Certificate

The class 1 medical is the highest standard, giving the greatest privileges (for example, most professional flight crew require a class 1 medical) and a 'higher' medical certificate also has the privileges and validity of a lower one. In other words, a class 1 medical certificate includes the privileges and validities of class 2 and LAPL medical certificates; a class 2 medical certificate includes the privileges and validities of a LAPL medical certificate.

The requirements for EASA medical certificates are set out in EASA legislation known as 'PART-MED'. Most of this documentation is of greater interest to doctors than pilots, but it does set out the standards and procedures a doctor must use before issuing an aviation medical certificate. Generally, an aviation medical certificate may only be issued by a doctor who is designated as an **Aero-Medical Examiner** (**AME**). EASA does allow an individual competent authority to decide that LAPL medical certificates can also be issued by a **General Medical Practitioner** (**GMP**).

The period of validity of an aviation medical certificate is stated on the certificate itself, and are normally based on the class of medical and the age of the holder. Those periods of validity are:

United Kingdom Civil Aviation Authority EUROPEAN UNION Class 1 MEDICAL CERTIFICATE pertaining to a Part-FCL Licence Issued in accordance with Part-Med This medical certificate complies with ICAO standards, except the LAPL certificate.	I	Licensing Authority: **United Kingdom**
	III	Certificate Number: (CAA Ref) GBR - **123456E**
	IV	Last and first name of holder: (Surname, Forename) **Pilot, A**
	XIV	Date of birth: (dd, mm, yy) **29/09/1999**
	VI	Nationality: **British**

Figure AL10.1
A pilot's medical certificate will state the class of the medical, the period of validity and any specific limitations or endorsements.

Class 1 medical certificate	
Age	Period of validity
Up to 40	12 months
40-60	12 months, or 6 months if the holder is engaged in single-pilot commercial air transport operations carrying passengers
Above 60	6 months

Figure AL10.2
The periods of validity of an EASA 'PART-MED' Class One medical certificate.

Class 2 medical certificate	
Age	Period of validity
Up to 40	60 months (a medical certificate issued prior to reaching the age of 40 shall cease to be valid after the licence holder reaches the age of 42)
40 to 50	24 months (a medical certificate issued prior to reaching the age of 50 shall cease to be valid after the licence holder reaches the age of 51
Above 50	12 months

Figure AL10.3
The periods of validity of an EASA 'PART-MED' Class Two medical certificate.

LAPL medical certificate	
Age	Period of validity
Up to 40	60 months (a medical certificate issued prior to reaching the age of 40 shall cease to be valid after the licence holder reaches the age of 42)
Above 50	24 months

Figure AL10.4
The periods of validity of an EASA LAPL medical certificate.

These validity periods are calculated from the date of the medical assessment. An assessment may take place up to 45 days in advance of the expiry date of a medical certificate, in which case the validity period starts from when the previous certificate would expire (so the holder is not disadvantaged by having the assessment before the previous certificate expires).

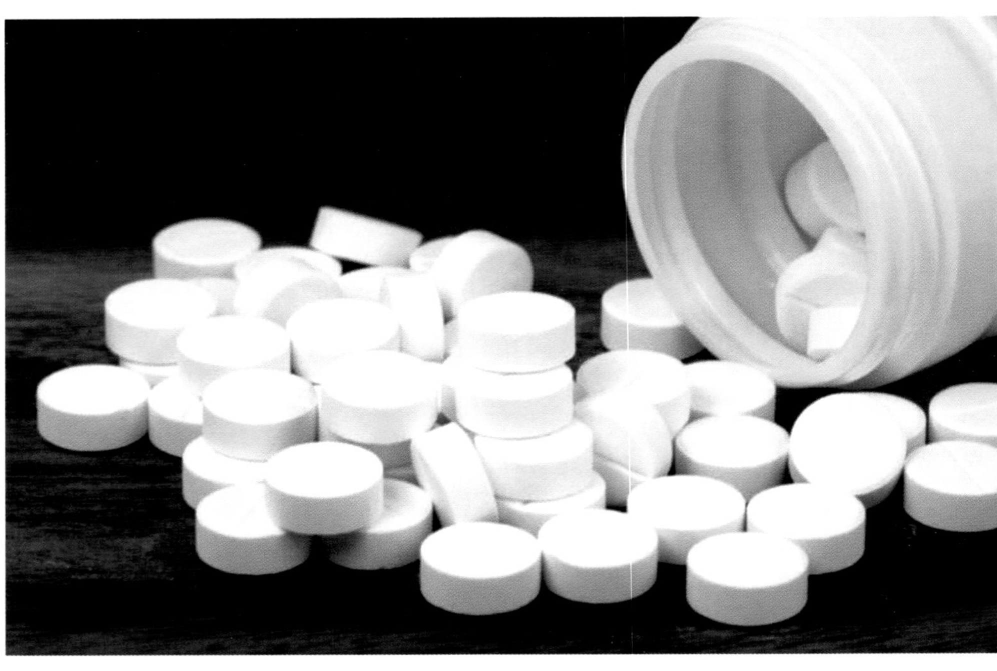

Figure AL10.5
Taking medicine, even one which can be obtained 'over the counter', may be incompatible with flying aircraft. If in doubt, seek medical advice.

Of course, even a pilot who holds a valid medical certificate may not be medically fit to fly at all times during that period of validity. Some medical conditions that make a pilot unfit to fly may be of a very temporary nature (for example a cold or an infection) and the intelligent pilot will know that there are times when the state of body or mind is simply not compatible with the responsibility of flying an aircraft. Nevertheless, to emphasis the point EASA specifies medical circumstances when pilots must not fly:

- If a pilot is aware of any decrease in medical fitness which might render him or her unable to safely exercise the licence privileges;
- If the pilot is taking or using any prescribed or non-prescribed medication which is likely to interfere with the safe exercise of the licence privileges;
- If the pilot has received any medical, surgical or other treatment that is likely to interfere with flight safety.

This list might be considered to be no more than common sense, but it is worth noting that even many well-known non-prescription ('over-the-counter') medicines may have side-effects which are not compatible with the responsibilities of flying an aircraft.

In addition to the above list, there are specific medical conditions or circumstances when a pilot not only must not fly, but must also seek the advice of an AME (or GMP for a LAPL medical certificate holder, if permitted). These conditions or circumstances are those when the holder of a medical certificate:

- Has undergone a surgical operation or invasive procedure;
- Has commenced the regular use of any medication;
- Has suffered any significant personal injury involving incapacity to function as a member of the flight crew;
- Has been suffering from any significant illness involving incapacity to function as a member of the flight crew;
- Is pregnant;
- Has been admitted to hospital or medical clinic;
- First requires correcting lenses.

In all the above circumstances, the medical certificate holder must seek advice *"...without undue delay"*.

Additionally, EASA states that advice should be sought from an AME if a medical certificate holder has been suffering from any illness that involves *"incapacity to function as a member of the flight crew"* for a period of at least 21 days.

The responsibilities and limitations associated with holding a medical certificate apply equally to a student pilot, as a student pilot must not fly solo unless he or she holds a valid medical certificate appropriate for the licence being trained for.

Private Pilot Licence (PPL) privileges

The most popular type of pilot licence (in terms of number of licences held), in almost any state with a developed civil aviation infrastructure is the **Private Pilot Licence** (**PPL**). For many aspiring pilots the PPL is the basic licence which is the initial goal of their flying career. An EASA PPL is valid throughout the EASA states and so can be used to fly aircraft registered in any EASA state. As an ICAO-compliant licence (that is, it complies with ICAO Annex 1, 'Personnel Licencing'), the EASA PPL is also widely recognised outside Europe so that in most countries of the world, an EASA PPL holder can fly an aircraft registered in that state with limited formalities and paperwork.

A private pilot is defined as a pilot who holds a licence which prohibits the piloting of aircraft in operations for which remuneration is given. **Remuneration** can be defined as receiving money or some other valuable compensation, and this key limitation can also be expressed as prohibiting a private pilot from flying for 'hire or reward' or 'valuable consideration'. The documentation which governs the privileges of an EASA PPL are quite explicit on this point, and state that the privileges of the holder of a PPL are to act without remuneration as PIC or co-pilot engaged in non-commercial operations.

This fundamental limitation of a Private Pilot Licence is one which the aviation authorities take very seriously. Any PPL thinking of charging for flying services should check the relevant EASA and national legislation very carefully as any suggestion that a private pilot is engaging in commercial operations, no matter how informal or unofficial, is very likely to make the pilot liable to prosecution. Furthermore, it is highly likely that both aircraft and personal insurance cover will be invalidated by any kind of illegal commercial operation.

The one exception to this rule is that the holder of a PPL with instructor or examiner privileges may receive remuneration for:

- Providing flight instruction for the LAPL or the PPL;
- The conduct of skill tests and proficiency checks for these licences;
- The ratings and certificates attached to these licences.

A PPL (and for that matter, any other EASA pilot licence) will be issued for a specific aircraft category. **Aircraft category** means the categorisation of an aircraft according to basic characteristics, for example aeroplane, helicopter, airship, sailplane (glider) or balloon. The two most common categories of aircraft on any civil register are 'aeroplane' and 'helicopter'.

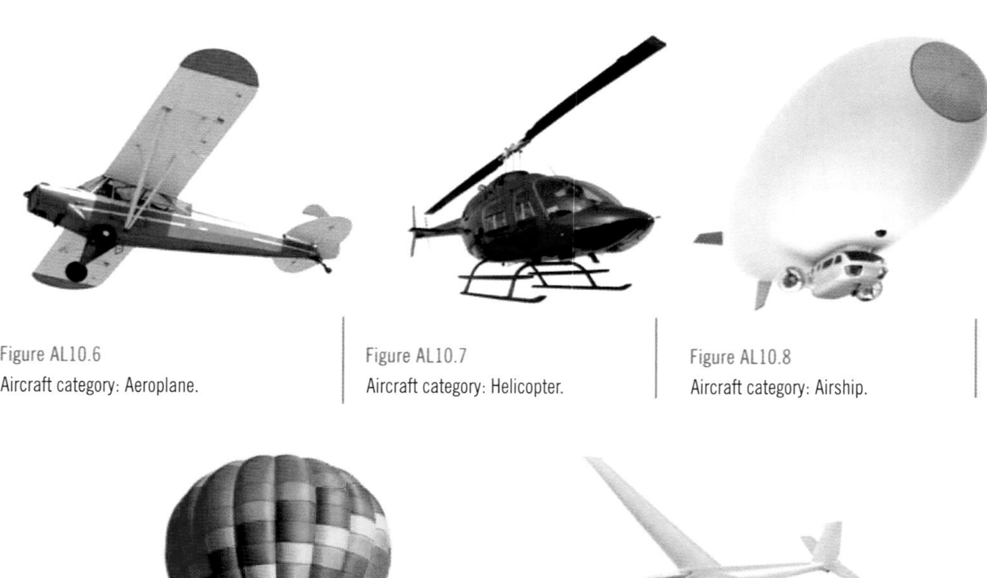

Figure AL10.6
Aircraft category: Aeroplane.

Figure AL10.7
Aircraft category: Helicopter.

Figure AL10.8
Aircraft category: Airship.

Figure AL10.10
Aircraft category: Balloon.

Figure AL10.9
Aircraft category: Sailplane (also known as a 'glider').

A PPL for aeroplanes – abbreviated to PPL(A) – will be granted only upon successful completion of a course of training, the key elements of which are:

- Complete at least 45 hours of flight instruction in aeroplanes or Touring Motor Gliders (TMG), including at least 25 hours of dual flight instruction and 10 hours of supervised solo flight time. The 10 hours of solo flight time must include at least 5 hours of solo cross country time. Up to 5 hours of the 45 hours total may be completed in a **Flight Simulation Training Device** (**FSTD**).
- Successfully complete at least 1 solo cross-country flight of at least 150 nautical miles, during which full stop landings are made at 2 aerodromes different from the aerodrome of departure.
- Pass examination(s) on the theoretical knowledge subjects of air law, operational procedures, communications, meteorology, navigation, principles of flight, flight performance and planning, aircraft general knowledge and human performance.
- Pass a skill test on the appropriate aircraft category.

Flight time for aeroplanes and TMG means the total time from the moment an aircraft first moves for the purpose of taking off, until the moment it finally comes to rest at the end of the flight.

A **Touring Motor Glider** (**TMG**) is defined as a specific class of powered sailplane having an integrally mounted, non-retractable engine and a non-retractable propeller. It must be capable of taking off and climbing under its own power.

A PPL for helicopters – abbreviated to PPL(H) – will be granted only upon successful completion of a course of training, the key elements of which are:

- Complete at least 45 hours of flight instruction in helicopters, including at least 25 hours of dual flight instruction and 10 hours of supervised solo flight time. The 10 hours of solo flight time must include at least 5 hours of solo cross country time. Up to 5 hours of the 45 hours total may be completed in a **Flight and Navigation Procedures Trainer** (**FNPT**) or **Full Flight Simulator** (**FFS**).
- Successfully complete at least 1 solo cross-country flight of at least 100 nautical miles, during which full stop landings are made at 2 aerodromes different from the aerodrome of departure.
- Of the 45 hours flight instruction time, at least 35 hours must be completed on the same type of helicopter as that used for the skill test.
- Pass examination(s) on the theoretical knowledge subjects of air law, operational procedures, communications, meteorology, navigation, principles of flight, flight performance and planning, aircraft general knowledge and human performance.
- Pass a skill test on the appropriate aircraft category.

Flight time for helicopters means the total time from the moment a helicopter's rotor blades start turning until the moment the helicopter finally comes to rest at the end of the flight, and the rotor blades are stopped.

As a general principle, all flight instruction must be completed in the same category of aircraft as the licence being trained for.

A student pilot must not fly solo unless authorised to do so and supervised by a flight instructor. Before first solo flight, a student pilot must be at least 16 years of age (in the case of aeroplanes and helicopters).

Some further flying training definitions:

Dual flight instruction time	Flight time during which a person is receiving flight instruction from a properly authorised instructor.
Solo flight time	Flight time during which the student pilot is the sole occupant of the aircraft.
Cross-country	A flight between a point of departure and a point of arrival following a pre-planned route, using standard navigation procedures.
Skill test	A demonstration of skill for licence or rating issue, including any oral examination the examiner may require.

Figure AL10.11
Definitions in relation to flying training.

Pilot's Logbook — Airplan Flight Equipment — www.afeonline.com

Date	Make Model Variant	Registration	Name (PIC)	Designation	Departure Place	Time	Arrival Place	Time	Day SE PIC	Day SE Dual	Day ME PIC	Day ME Dual	Night SE PIC	Night SE Dual	Night ME PIC	Night ME Dual	FT	IFR	ACF	T/O & Landing Day	T/O & Landing Night	Remarks
02/03/16	C152	G-BDEX	SMITH	P/UT	HAWARDEN	1105	LOCAL	1210		1·05												EXERCISE 6
15/06/16	HR200	G-BXVO	SELF	P1	COVENTRY	1445	CRANFIELD	1530	0·45											1 1		EXERCISE 18 VIA OLNEY
28/10/16	PA-28	G-BHAX	SELF	P1	SOUTHEND	1705	WELSHPOOL	1900	0·45				1·10				0·15	1.10		1	1 2	VIA CFD AND HON

Figure AL10.12
A pilot must maintain a logbook to record details of all flight where he or she acted as a member of the flight crew.

A pilot (including a student pilot) must keep a reliable record of the details of all flights flown, in a form and manner established by the competent authority. In practice this means recording flight details in some form of **pilot logbook**. This logbook should contain detailed instructions on how to record flight details in accordance with EASA guidance but in general details of each flight (for example: date, flight time, departure and destination, capacity in which the pilot operated) must be recorded for any flight where the pilot acts as a member of the flight crew. Entries in a flight crew logbook should be made as soon as possible after the flight and all entries should be made in ink or indelible pencil. And if you can find an indelible pencil in this day and age, you probably deserve some sort of award. It is also important to know that a pilot's licence is highly likely to be suspended or revoked if any entries in the pilot's logbook are falsified.

The minimum age for the grant of a PPL is 17 years, there is no maximum age limit and in fact there are a number of active pilots their 90s.

The minimum medical standard for holding an EASA PPL is a Class 2 medical certificate. Licence privileges can only be exercised if the pilot has a valid medical certificate and complies with any limitations contained in that certificate.

An aeroplane or helicopter pilot who is required to use the radio must have a **language proficiency** endorsement on their licence, indicating their competency in either the English language, or the language used for radio communications for the intended flight. Language proficiency will be assessed both in the use of radio phraseologies and plain language, as one of six levels. The minimum language proficiency level required for endorsement on an EASA licence is Level 4 (Operational).

Level 1	Pre-elementary
Level 2	Elementary
Level 3	Pre-operational
Level 4	Operational
Level 5	Extended
Level 6	Expert

Figure AL10.13
The ICAO levels of language proficiency.

The PPL gives the holder the right to fly with passengers, but in order to exercise this privilege there is a 'recent experience' requirement to ensure that the pilot's skills are current. In order to carry passengers a pilot must have carried out, in the preceding 90 days, at least 3 take-offs, approaches and landings in an aircraft of the same type or class,

Figure AL10.14
A qualified pilot is only permitted to carry passengers if the 'recency' requirements have been met.

or a **Full Flight Simulator (FFS)** representing that type or class. The terms 'type' and 'class' are defined later. If a pilot needs to carry out a flight with an instructor or examiner to comply with this requirement before carrying passengers, the instructor or examiner on board those flights is not considered to be a passenger.

Figure AL10.15
The holder of a PPL without any form of 'Instrument Rating' may not fly under Instrument Flight Rules (IFR). Therefore, the pilot must comply with Visual Meteorological Conditions (VMC) minima or Special VFR minima where applicable at all times.

Unless an aeroplane or helicopter pilot holds a valid Instrument Rating (described later), he or she is limited to operating under Visual Flight Rules (VFR) or Special VFR where applicable. This means that the pilot must ensure that at all times the aircraft remains in conditions no worse than the VMC minima or Special VFR minima already described. Those with good memories may recall that in certain circumstances (for example, below 3000ft AMSL and at less than 140 knots indicated airspeed), the VMC minima may permit VFR flight in flight visibility as low as 1500 meters (or even less for helicopters). Any pilot who has flown VFR in such visibilities knows just how challenging such a flight is likely to be, which reinforces the point that just because something is legal, that doesn't automatically imply that it is safe in all circumstances. This is just another example of where pilot judgement is required to make the differentiation between what is legal and what is safe. The other implication of this licence restriction is that a pilot without some form of Instrument Rating may not fly under Instrument Flight Rules (IFR) at any time, even when in VMC.

Figure AL10.16
Unless the pilot hold an appropriate rating he or she cannot fly at night.

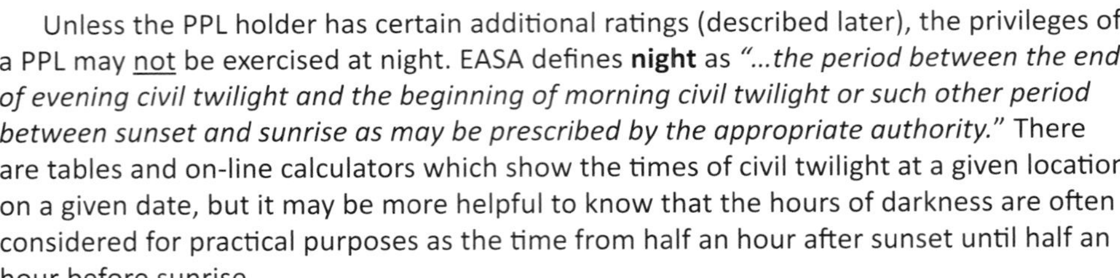

Unless the PPL holder has certain additional ratings (described later), the privileges of a PPL may <u>not</u> be exercised at night. EASA defines **night** as *"...the period between the end of evening civil twilight and the beginning of morning civil twilight or such other period between sunset and sunrise as may be prescribed by the appropriate authority."* There are tables and on-line calculators which show the times of civil twilight at a given location on a given date, but it may be more helpful to know that the hours of darkness are often considered for practical purposes as the time from half an hour after sunset until half an hour before sunrise.

The competent authority which has issued a pilot's licence also has the power to limit, suspend or revoke it. Circumstances that might give cause for such action include:

- Obtaining the pilot licence by falsification of submitted documentary evidence;
- Falsification of logbook and licence records;
- The licence holder no longer complies with the applicable requirements of Part-FCL;
- Exercising the privileges of a licence when adversely affected by alcohol or drugs;
- Non-compliance with the applicable operational requirements;
- Evidence of malpractice or fraudulent use of the licence.

A valid licence and a valid medical certificate must always be carried by the pilot when exercising the privileges of the licence. The pilot must also carry some form of 'personal identification document' containing his/her photo.

Light Aircraft Pilot Licence (LAPL) privileges

The **Light Aircraft Pilot Licence** (**LAPL**) is a licence which can be obtained after less comprehensive training than for a PPL, and so it has privileges which are more restrictive than those of a PPL in certain aspects. A LAPL is recognised throughout the EASA states and so can be used to fly an EASA-registered aircraft. However, because the LAPL is not an ICAO-complaint licence (it does not meet the requirements of ICAO Annex 1, 'Personnel Licencing'), the use of a LAPL to fly an aircraft registered outside the EASA states will require individual agreement with that state's National Aviation Authority.

The basic privilege of the holder of a LAPL is to act without remuneration as Pilot In Command (PIC) in non-commercial operations on the appropriate aircraft category. As with a PPL holder, there are severe consequences for an LAPL holder who engages in any form of aircraft operation which could be considered an illegal commercial operation.

Figure AL10.17
Despite its size, the Piper Matrix has a Maximum Take-Off Weight (MTOW) of just under 2000kg.

A LAPL for aeroplanes – abbreviated to LAPL(A) – will be granted upon successful completion of a course of training, the key elements of which are:

- Complete at least 30 hours of flight instruction in aeroplanes or Touring Motor Gliders (TMG), including at least 15 hours of dual flight instruction in the class (aeroplane or TMG) in which the skill test will be taken.
- Complete at least 6 hours of supervised solo flight time, including at least 3 hours of solo cross country time.
- Successfully complete at least 1 solo cross-country flight of at least 80 nautical miles, during which a full stop landing is made at an aerodrome different from the aerodrome of departure.
- Pass examination(s) on the theoretical knowledge subjects of air law, operational procedures, communications, meteorology, navigation, principles of flight, flight performance and planning, aircraft general knowledge and human performance.
- Pass a skill test on the appropriate aircraft category.

A LAPL for helicopters – abbreviated to LAPL(H) – will be granted upon successful completion of a course of training, the key elements of which are:

- Complete at least 40 hours of flight instruction in helicopters, including at least 20 hours of dual flight instruction.
- Complete at 10 hours of supervised solo flight time. The 10 hours of solo flight time must include at least 5 hours of solo cross country time.
- Successfully complete at least 1 solo cross-country flight of at least 80 nautical miles, during which a full stop landing is made at an aerodrome different from the aerodrome of departure.
- Of the 40 hours flight instruction time, at least 35 hours must be completed on the same type of helicopter as that used for the skill test.
- Pass examination(s) on the theoretical knowledge subjects of air law, operational procedures, communications, meteorology, navigation, principles of flight, flight performance and planning, aircraft general knowledge and human performance.
- Pass a skill test on the appropriate aircraft category.

As for a PPL student, a student pilot must not fly solo unless authorised to do so and supervised by a flight instructor. Before first solo flight, a student pilot must be at least 16 years of age (in the case of aeroplanes and helicopters).

The minimum age for the grant of a LAPL is 17 years, there is no maximum age limit.

The minimum medical standard for holding a LAPL is a LAPL medical certificate. Licence privileges can only be exercised if the pilot has a valid medical certificate and complies with any limitations contained in that certificate.

A LAPL holder required to use the radio must have a 'language proficiency' endorsement on their licence, as already described.

The privileges a LAPL(A) are to act as PIC on land-based single-engine piston aeroplanes or TMGs with a maximum certificated take-off mass of 2000kg or less, carrying a maximum of 3 passengers, so that there are never more than 4 persons on board the aircraft. The holder of a LAPL(A) can only carry passengers after completing, since the issue of the licence, 10 hours of flight time as PIC on aeroplanes or TMGs.

In order to carry passengers a pilot must have carried out, in the preceding 90 days, at least 3 take-offs, approaches and landings in an aircraft of the same type or class, or an FFS representing that type or class (the terms 'type' and 'class' are defined later). If a pilot needs to carry out a flight with an instructor or examiner to comply with this requirement before carrying passengers, the instructor or examiner on board those flights is not considered to be a passenger.

Further, a LAPL(A) holder shall only exercise the privileges of their licence when they have completed, in the last 24 months, as pilot of aeroplanes or TMG:

- at least 12 hours of flight time as PIC, including 12 take-offs and landings; and
- refresher training of at least 1 hour of total flight time with an instructor.

The privileges of a LAPL(H) are to act as PIC on single-engine helicopters with a maximum certificated take-off mass of 2000kg or less, carrying a maximum of 3 passengers, such that there are never more than 4 persons on board.

A LAPL(H) holder can only exercise the privileges of their licence on a specific type of helicopter when they have completed, on that type of helicopter, in the last 12 months:

- at least 6 hours of flight time as PIC, including 6 take-offs, approaches and landings; and
- refresher training of at least 1 hour total flight time with an instructor.

A LAPL holder is limited to operating under Visual Flight Rules (VFR), so the pilot must ensure that at all times the flight remains in conditions no worse than the VMC minima. Unless the LAPL holder has certain additional ratings (described later), the privileges of a LAPL may <u>not</u> be exercised at night.

Class Rating

Even the casual observer at an average General Aviation (GA) airfield will notice the wide variety of aircraft types around and it does not take very much imagination to realise that there must be significant variation between different models of aircraft – not just in terms of handling and performance characteristics, but also equipment and systems. It follows that a pilot's licence does not permit a pilot to just jump into any aircraft of the category they are licenced for and fly it, but rather further training or experience requirements may apply.

The term 'class' applies to aeroplanes but not helicopters, and a **class of aeroplane** is a categorisation of single-pilot aeroplanes which do not require a 'type rating' (described later). An aeroplane class describes a group of aeroplanes which do not require a type rating and have broadly similar characteristics. The most common EASA aeroplane classes are:

Aeroplane Class	EASA Class Rating	Description
Single-engine Piston (land)	**SEP (land)**	A single pilot land-based aeroplane of any manufacturer, with a single piston engine
Single-engine Piston (sea)	**SEP (sea)**	A single pilot water-based aeroplane of any manufacturer, with a single piston engine
Multi-engine Piston (land)	**MEP (land)**	A single pilot land-based aeroplane of any manufacturer, with multiple piston engines
Multi-engine Piston (sea)	**MEP (sea)**	A single pilot water-based aeroplane of any manufacturer, with multiple piston engines
Touring Motor Glider	**TMG**	All TMGs of any manufacturer, with an integrally mounted, non-retractable engine and a non-retractable propeller

Figure AL10.18
Aeroplane class ratings.

Figure AL10.19
A Cessna TTX is within the Single Engine Piston (SEP) class rating.

Figure AL10.20
A Maule – an example of an aeroplane in the Single Engine Piston (sea) class rating.

Figure AL10.21
A Beechcraft Baron is within the Multi Engine Piston (MEP) class rating.

Figure AL10.22
A rare flying machine – a Multi Engine Piston seaplane (in this case an AeroVolga La-8), in the class rating MEP (Sea).

Figure AL10.23
An appropriately registered SF25 Falke Touring Motor Glider (TMG).

The privileges of a class rating are to act as pilot on the class of aeroplane specified in the rating. Of course, each class rating may contain many different types and models of aeroplane. Therefore, EASA requires that any pilot wishing to fly a different 'variant' of aeroplane within a class rating must undertake either 'differences' or 'familiarisation' training as appropraite.

Differences training requires both the acquisition of additional knowledge and training on an appropriate training device or the aircraft itself.

Familiarisation training requires only the acquisition of additional knowledge.

EASA specify that certain aeroplane features require 'differences training' before a pilot can fly an aeroplane with that feature. The difference training requirement applies to the following features:

- Variable pitch propellers (VP)
- Retractable undercarriage (RU)
- Turbo or super-charged engines (T)
- Cabin pressurisation (P)
- Tail wheel (TW)
- Electronic Flight Instrument System (EFIS)
- Single Lever Power Control (SPLC)

Differences training must be entered into the pilot's logbook and signed by the instructor as appropriate when complete.

Figure AL10.24
Variable Pitch propeller (VP): the blue 'PROP' lever next to the throttle control of this PA28 Arrow indicates a pitch control lever, used to control a variable pitch propeller. Incidentally, the three green lights and 'Gear' lever to the left of the throttle indicate that this aircraft also has retractable undercarriage.

Figure AL10.25
Retractable Undercarriage (RU): an aircraft (in this case a Piper Seneca, in the MEP class rating) with retractable undercarriage.

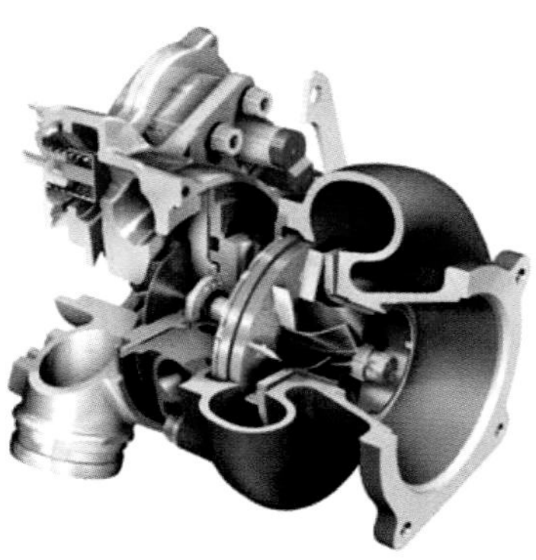

Figure AL10.26
Turbo or super-charged engines (T): a piston engine fitted with a turbo charger or supercharger is not to be confused with a turbine engine – which is effectively a jet engine.

Figure AL10.27
Cabin pressurisation (CP): An aircraft with cabin pressurisation means that the aircraft can fly at higher altitudes without the occupants having to use oxygen equipment (such as oxygen masks).

Figure AL10.28
Tail wheel (TW): an aeroplane with a tailwheel has very different taxi, take-off and landing characteristics to a 'nose wheel' aeroplane.

Figure AL10.29
Electronic Flight Instrument System (EFIS): replacing tradition 'round dial' flight instruments and otherwise commonly known as a 'glass cockpit'.

Figure AL10.30
Single Lever Power Control (SPLC): the two engines of this Diamond Twin Star are each controlled by a single lever.

Because of the wide variety of aeroplane types which can be found within a single 'class rating', the matter of switching from one aeroplane model to another needs to be considered carefully. Even if the pilot is planning to fly an aeroplane model for which he or she already holds the appropriate class rating and differences training (for example, an SEP with retractable undercarriage), the legal minimum of familiarisation training only may not be sufficient for practical purposes. The aeroplane may have equipment, or features, or handling characteristics, for which the pilot is well-advised to receive some form of training. In practice, it is most common that when a pilot wants to fly a new variant within a class rating, some form of actual 'on aeroplane' training – for example a 'checkout flight' – is very common and indeed may be a requirement of the aeropane's insurer.

Except for the holder of a LAPL, Sailplane Pilot Licence (SPL) or Balloon Pilot Licence (BPL), a pilot must not exercise the privileges of his or her licence unless they have an appropriate and valid class rating (or type rating). Passing the skill test for the issue of a PPL(A) also gives the privilege to fly the class of aeroplane used for the test.

To add a further class rating, the pilot must meet training and experience requirements as specified for the particular class rating, and pass a skill test.

Single engine, single pilot class ratings are valid for a period of 24 months. Other class ratings are valid for 12 months.

Revalidation means the action or specified requirements taken within the period of validity of a rating or certificate which allows the holder to continue exercising the appropriate privileges for a further specified period.

To revalidate an SEP or TMG class rating, the pilot has two options:

1. Pass a proficiency check in the appropriate aeroplane class within 3 months of the expiry date of the rating.

OR

2. Within the 12 months preceding the expiry of the rating, complete at least 12 hours of flight time in the relevant aeroplane class, including at least 6 hours as PIC and 12 take-offs and landings. Additionally, complete a training flight of at least 1 hour with a flight instructor (FI) or a class rating instructor (CRI). The training flight is not required if a pilot has completed a class or type rating 'proficiency check' or skill test in any other class or type of aeroplane.

A **Proficiency check** is the demonstration of skill to revalidate or renew ratings, and including such oral examination as may be required.

To revalidate an MEP rating, the pilot must pass a proficiency check in the relevant class of aeroplane or an FSTD representing that class within the 3 months immediately preceding the expiry date of the rating. The pilot must also complete 1 route sector as pilot of the relevant class of aeroplane or Full Flight Simulator (FFS) with an examiner, this may be flown during the proficiency check. This last requirement is not necessary if the pilot has instead flown at least 10 route sectors in the relevant class of aeroplane during the period of validity of the class rating.

A **route sector** is a flight comprising take-off, departure, cruise of not less than 15 minutes, arrival, approach and landing phases.

If a class rating has expired, some form of rating 'renewal' will be required, this normally takes the form of refresher training and a proficiency check.

Renewal means the action or specified requirements taken after a rating or certificate has expired which allows the holder to once again exercise the appropriate privileges for a further specified period.

Certain other class ratings exist, including those for singe engine turbo-prop (SET) aeroplanes from a specific manufacturer, or specific aeroplane series, for example 'CESSNA SET' or 'PA-46 SET'. Some single pilot aeroplanes may be classified as a **High Performance Aeroplane** (**HPA**). These are aeroplanes which are certificated for **Single Pilot** (**SP**) operation but which have performance, systems and navigation capabilities more usually associated with **Multi Pilot** (MP) aeroplane types, and regularly operate within the same airspace. For this reason additional training and qualification requirements apply for a private pilot wishing to operate a HPA.

Figure AL10.31
A 'Piper SET' aircraft (in this case a Piper M600).

Specific arrangements exist for LAPL(A) holders wanting to fly a different aircraft type than that used for the initial skill test. Before a LAPL(A) holder can exercise the privileges of the licence on a variant of aeroplane different to the one used for the skill test, the pilot must undertake differences or familiarisation training. The differences training shall be entered in the pilot's logbook and signed by the instructor. To fly a class of aeroplane different to that used for the initial skill test, the LAPL(A) holder must complete 3 hours of flight instruction in the other class, including 10 dual take-offs and landings; and 10 supervised solo take-offs and landings. Additionally the pilot must pass a skill test which will include demonstrating adequate theoretical knowledge of the other class in the subjects of operational procedures, flight performance and planning and aircraft general knowledge.

Type Rating

If an aircraft type is not covered by a class rating, flying it requires a valid **Type Rating**. A type rating applies to all helicopters and to aeroplanes which are too complex to be covered by a class rating. A type rating will normally include all aircraft of the same basic design including all modifications, except those modifications which result in a change in handling or flight characteristics.

The privilege of the holder of a type rating is to act as pilot on the type of aircraft specified in the rating. An applicant for a type rating must complete a defined training course, including the mandatory training elements for the relevant type as defined by EASA or the competent authority. At the end of the course the applicant must pass a theoretical knowledge examination as well as a skill test. A type rating is valid for 12 months and the revalidation requirements are the same as for a MEP class rating – those requirements are to pass a proficiency check in the relevant aircraft type or a Flight Simulation Training Device (FSTD) representing that type, within the 3 months immediately preceding the expiry date of the type rating. The pilot must also complete 1 route sector as pilot of the relevant type of aircraft or FFS with an examiner, this may be flown during the proficiency check. This last requirement is not necessary if the pilot has instead flown at least 10 route sectors in the relevant aircraft type during the period of validity of the type rating. If a type rating has expired the pilot must undertake refresher training and pass a proficiency check

EASA publish lists of aeroplane and helicopter type ratings. Those lists indicate where differences training is required when moving between different variants within a type rating. If the variant has not been flown within a period of 2 years following the differences training, further differences training or a proficiency check in that variant is required to maintain the privileges. This requirement also applies to class ratings except those for SEP and TMG.

Figure AL10.32
Each helicopter type requires a separate type rating, there are no 'class ratings' for helicopters.

The privileges of an LAPL(H) are limited to the specific type and variant of helicopter in which the skill test was taken. This limitation may be removed by the pilot completing

Figure AL10.33
To fly this Citation Mustang a pilot will need to hold the appropriate Type Rating.

5 hours of flight instruction, including 15 dual take-offs, approaches and landings, 15 supervised solo take-offs, approaches and landings and a skill test. During this skill test, the applicant must also demonstrate to the examiner an adequate level of theoretical knowledge for the other type in the subjects of operational procedures, flight performance and planning and aircraft general knowledge.

Other Ratings and Certificates

The essential legal requirements in terms a pilot licence are that the licence itself is valid, that the appropriate medical certificate is valid and that the appropriate class or type rating is valid. Although the pilot licence gives the pilot a lot of freedom to fly, many pilots seek extra ratings to add to their licence, either to make the type of flying they want to do more practical, to accomplish a particular flying goal, or just to make flying even more enjoyable. Each rating has its own pre-entry and training requirements, the following is an overview of the EASA ratings available to add to an EASA pilot licence.

Figure AL10.34
An aerobatic rating allows the holder to explore advanced flight manoeuvres.

Aerobatic Rating
Permits the holder to undertake aerobatic flights. 'Aerobatic flight' means an intentional manoeuvre involving an abrupt change in an aircraft's attitude, an abnormal attitude, or abnormal acceleration, not necessary for normal flight or for instruction for licences or ratings other than the aerobatic rating.

En-route Instrument Rating (EIR)
Permits the holder to conduct flights by day under Instrument Flight Rules (IFR) in the en route phase of flight, in an aeroplane for which a class or type rating is held. The EIR privilege may be extended to conduct flights by night under IFR in the en route phase of flight if the pilot also holds a night rating

Figure AL10.35
The en-route instrument rating allows the holder to fly under Instrument Flight Rules (IFR) during the en-route phase of a flight.

Figure AL10.36
These particular test pilots test Airbus airliners.

Flight Test Rating
Permits the holder to act as PIC on category 1 or 2 flight tests.

Figure AL10.37
An Instrument Rating allows the holder to fly Instrument Flight Rules (IFR) during all phases of a flight.

Instrument Rating (IR)
Permits the holder to undertake operations under IFR with an IR appropriate to the category of aircraft.

Figure AL10.38
Certain high altitude airports may only be used by pilots holding a Mountain Rating. This spectacular airport is Courchevel in the Alps.

Mountain Rating
Permits the holder to conduct flights with aeroplanes or TMG to and from surfaces designated as requiring such a rating by the appropriate authorities.

Figure AL10.39
A Night Rating increases the pilot's flexibility when planning trips and opens up a very different aspect of flight.

Night Rating
Permits the privileges of a LAPL(A), PPL(A) or PPL(H) to be exercised in VFR conditions at night.

Figure AL10.40
Towing sailplanes or banners requires a specific rating.

Sailplane Towing and Banner Towing Ratings
Permits the holder to tow sailplanes or banners.

Progress Check

89 What is the periof of validity of a Class 2 medical certificate, if the holder is 30 years old?
90 What action must the holder of a Class 2 medical certificate take if he or she undergoes surgery or other invasive procedure?
91 What action must the holder of a Class 2 medical certificate take if he or she suffers from an illness making them unfit to fly for a period of longer than 21 days?
92 What is the basic limitation of a Private Pilot Licence in terms of remuneration?
93 How if 'flight time' defined for an aeroplane or TMG?
94 How if 'flight time' defined for a helicopter?
95 How is 'solo flight time' defined for a student pilot?
96 What is the 'recency' requirement for a PPL holder wishing to fly with passengers?
97 Can a PPL holder without additional rating fly under Instrument Flight Rules (IFR)?
98 Can a PPL holder without additional rating fly at night?
99 Give one example of circumstances which may lead to the competent authority limiting, suspending or revoking a pilot's licence.
100 What is the minimum medical standard for exercising the privileges of a LAPL?
101 What is the 'take-off mass' limitation for the holder of a LAPL?
102 What is the maximum number of passengers a LAPL holder may carry?
103 If the holder of an SEP class rating wishes to fly a variant with Retractable Undercarriage (RU) for the first time, what (if any) addition training is required?
104 What is 'familiarisation training'?
105 What is the period of validity of a SEP or TMG class rating?
106 What are the revalidation requirements of a SEP or TMG class rating.
107 What is the period of validity of a Type Rating?
108 Does a pilot require a specific rating to undertake aerobatic flight?

These questions are intended to test knowledge and reinforce some of the key learning points from this section. In answering these questions, a 'pass rate' of around 80% should be the target.

Model answers are found at page 147

AL11 National Procedures

National rules and procedures

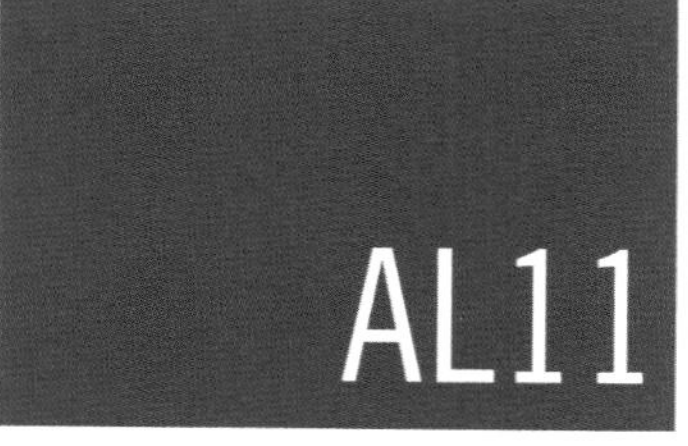

AL11 National Procedures

National rules and procedures

The following information applies to the **United Kingdom** (**UK**), which for the purposes of this publication consists of England, Wales, Scotland and Northern Ireland. It should be noted that some territories that might normally be considered to be part of the UK, such as the Channel Islands and the Isle of Man, have their own aviation legislation. Information in relation to UK rules and procedures is limited to those elements which are significantly different to the European or ICAO procedures described in the main text and is presented under the chapter headings used in sections AL1 – AL10.

Civil Aviation Authority

Figure AL11.1
The Civil Aviation Authority is the 'Competent Authority' for the United Kingdom.

International Aviation Law
The 'Competent Authority' for the United Kingdom is the **UK Civil Aviation Authority – CAA (www.caa.co.uk)**.

European Rules of the Air
The UK publishes its own rules of the air, which are enacted into UK law as **The Rules of the Air Regulations**. The UK Rules of the Air Regulations apply to all aircraft within the United Kingdom and all aircraft registered in the United Kingdom, wherever they may be. The key UK rules of the air which are additional or significantly different to SERA are as follows.

Aerobatic flight is not permitted in the UK over the congested area of any city, town or settlement; or within controlled airspace, except with the consent of the appropriate ATC unit. 'Aerobatic manoeuvres' includes loops, spins, rolls, bunts, stall turns, inverted flying and any other similar manoeuvre.

A **congested area** in relation to a city, town or settlement, means any area which is substantially used for residential, industrial, commercial or recreational purposes.

If an ATC unit has communicated an order of priority for landing, aircraft must approach to land in that order.

A 'flying machine' or glider must not land on a runway at an aerodrome if there are other aircraft on the runway, unless authorised to do so by an ATC unit.

A **flying machine** means an aeroplane, a powered lift tilt rotor aircraft, a Self Launching Motor Glider (SLMG), a helicopter or a gyroplane.

If take-offs and landings are not confined to a runway, when landing a flying machine or glider must leave clear on its left any aircraft which has landed, is already landing or is about to take-off. A flying machine or glider which is about to turn, must turn to the left if the commander of the aircraft is satisfied that such action will not interfere with other traffic movements. Unless otherwise authorised by an ATC unit, a flying machine which is about to take-off must take up position and manoeuvre in such a way as to leave clear on its left any aircraft which has already taken off or is about to take-off. Unless otherwise authorised by an ATC unit, a flying machine must move clear of the landing area as soon as possible after landing.

Other UK-specific regulations governing the operation of aircraft that have a UK 'national' Certificate of Airworthiness or national Permit to Fly are contained within the **UK Air Navigation Order (ANO).**

Figure AL11.2
Under the UK Rules of the Air Regulations, aerobatic flight is not permitted over a city, town or settlement.

Figure AL11.3
Details of unlicenced airfields within the UK are found in commercially produced flight guides such as the UK VFR Flight Guide.

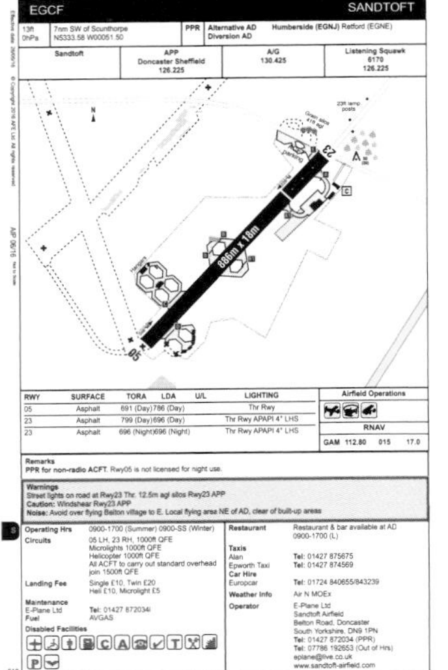

EGCF SANDTOFT

13ft 0hPa	7nm SW of Scunthorpe N5333.58 W00051.50	PPR	Alternative AD Diversion AD	Humberside (EGNJ) Retford (EGNE)

Sandtoft	APP Doncaster Sheffield 126.225	A/G 130.425	Listening Squawk 6170 126.225

RWY	SURFACE	TORA	LDA	U/L	LIGHTING
05	Asphalt	691 (Day)	786 (Day)		Thr Rwy
23	Asphalt	799 (Day)	696 (Day)		Thr Rwy APAPI 4° LHS
23	Asphalt	696 (Night)	696 (Night)		Thr Rwy APAPI 4° LHS

Airfield Operations

RNAV

GAM 112.80 015 17.0

Remarks
PPR for non-radio ACFT. Rwy05 is not licensed for night use.

Warnings
Street lights on road at Rwy23 Thr. 12.5m agl silos Rwy23 APP
Caution: Windshear Rwy23 APP
Noise: Avoid over flying Belton village to E. Local flying area NE of AD, clear of built-up areas

Operating Hrs	0900-1700 (Summer) 0900-SS (Winter)
Circuits	05 LH, 23 RH, 1000ft QFE Microlights 1000ft QFE Helicopter 1000ft QFE All ACFT to carry out standard overhead join 1500ft QFE
Landing Fee	Single £10, Twin £20 Heli £10, Microlight £5
Maintenance E-Plane Ltd	**Tel:** 01427 872034l
Fuel	AVGAS
Disabled Facilities	
Restaurant	Restaurant & bar available at AD 0900-1700 (L)
Taxis Alan Epworth Taxi	**Tel:** 01427 875675 **Tel:** 01427 874569
Car Hire Europcar	**Tel:** 01724 840655/843239
Weather Info	Air N MOEx
Operator	E-Plane Ltd Sandtoft Airfield Belton Road, Doncaster South Yorkshire, DN9 1PN **Tel:** 01427 872034 (PPR) **Tel:** 07786 192653 (Out of Hrs) eplane@live.co.uk www.sandtoft-airfield.com

616

Aerodromes

Within the UK there are three types of aerodrome; **Government** (almost always a military airfield); **Licenced** (the airfield has been inspected and approved by the CAA); and **Unlicensed** (which are not inspected by the CAA). As a general rule, commercial operations such as the carriage of fare-paying passengers and/or cargo can only take place at Government or licensed airfields. Details of licensed airfields are found in the UK AIP, in some circumstances an airfield may only be licensed during part of its opening hours.

Unlicensed airfields are not listed in the UK AIP, details of such airfields are normally found in commercially-produced flight guides and other non-official sources. Some unlicensed airfields may have features (such as obstructions, surface state, lack of markings, non-aviation usage etc.) which would not be acceptable at a licensed airfield.

An airfield may require that prior permission is obtained before using the airfield, in aeronautical publications such an airfield may be annotated as **PPR**, meaning **Prior Permission Required**. PPR must normally requested by telephone or e-mail as part of the pre-flight planning process. Most airfields in the UK are privately-owned and may require PPR to regulate airfield movements, integrate with non-aviation activities or to ensure that visiting pilots receive a briefing on the use of the airfield. A pilot who uses a 'PPR' airfield without first obtaining prior permission may be risking not only their own safety (and that of their passengers), but also the safety of other users of the airfield.

An aircraft must not taxi on the apron or the manoeuvring area of an uncontrolled aerodrome in the UK without the permission of the person in charge of the aerodrome, or the flight information service notified at the aerodrome. A person or vehicle must not go onto any part of a UK aerodrome without the permission of the person in charge of that aerodrome and must comply with any conditions of that permission. A person or vehicle must not go onto or move on the manoeuvring area of an aerodrome which provides an ATC service or flight information service without the permission of that service, and must comply with any conditions of permission.

PPR

Figure AL11.4
Prior Permission Required (PPR) means just that – prior permission is required before using the airfield. Failure to obtain PPR can create both legal and safety risks.

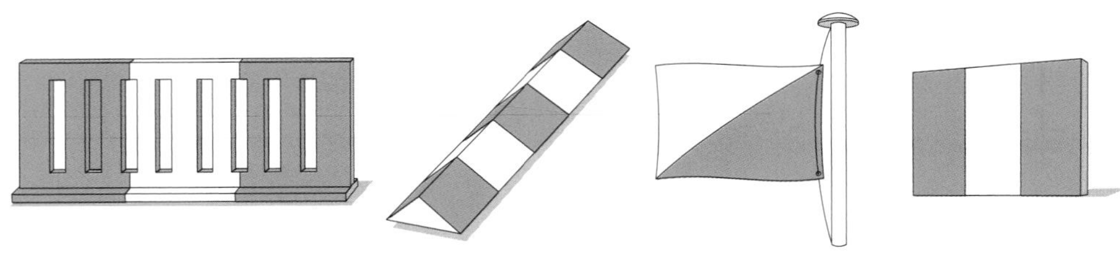

Figure AL11.5
At a UK aerodrome orange and white markers may be used to designate an area, runway, taxiway or apron which is unfit for the movement of aircraft.

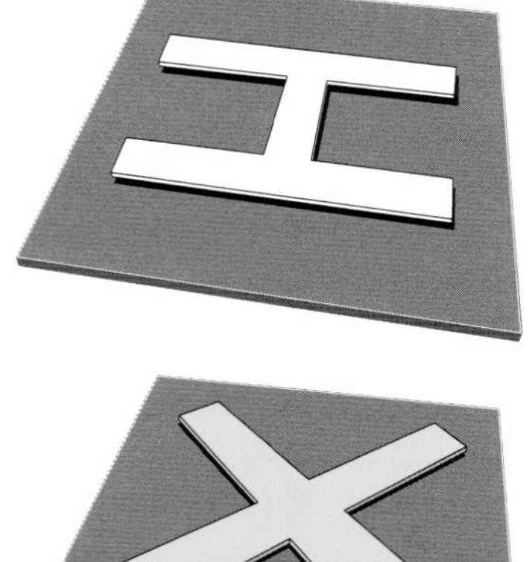

Figure AL11.6
A white 'H' indicates an area of an aerodrome for the take-off and landing of helicopters.

Figure AL11.7
A yellow cross indicates an area on an aerodrome where for tow ropes, banners and similar articles to be picked up and dropped.

An area of paved runway, taxiway or apron which is unfit for the movement of aircraft may be designated by orange and white markers. Orange and white triangular markers and flags indicate the boundary of an unpaved area which is unfit for the movement of aircraft. Orange and white boards may be used to designate the boundary of an aerodrome.

A white 'H' indicates an area of an aerodrome which must be used only for the taking off and landing of helicopters.

A yellow cross with two arms at right angles, indicates an area on an aerodrome where tow ropes, banners and similar articles towed by aircraft must be picked up and dropped.

Black numerals in two-figure groups on a yellow background indicate the direction for take-off or the runway in use. Where parallel runways exist, the letter(s) L (left), LC (left centre), C (centre), RC (right centre) and R (right) may be used.

Figure AL11.8
A two-number group on a yellow background indicates the direction for take-off or the runway in use.

The UK CAA requires that aircraft must not take-off or land within the congested area of any city, town or settlement except at an aerodrome (and in accordance with procedures notified by the CAA) or at another landing site and with the permission of the CAA. Furthermore, an aircraft must not land or take-off within 1000 metres of an open-air assembly of more than 1000 people except at an aerodrome (in accordance with procedures notified by the CAA) or if at another landing site, in accordance with procedures notified by the CAA and with the written permission of the organiser of the assembly.

Figure AL11.9
The UK CAA has established specific rules in relation to picking up, towing and dropping banners and other articles.

An aircraft must not take-off from a UK aerodrome when towing tow ropes, banners or similar articles except by arrangement made with the air traffic control unit at the aerodrome or the person in charge of the aerodrome.

Tow ropes, banners or similar articles towed by aircraft must not be picked up by, or dropped from, an aircraft at an aerodrome except by arrangement made with the air traffic control unit at the aerodrome; or the person in charge of the aerodrome; or in the area designated by the appropriate markings but only when the aircraft is flying in the direction appropriate for landing.

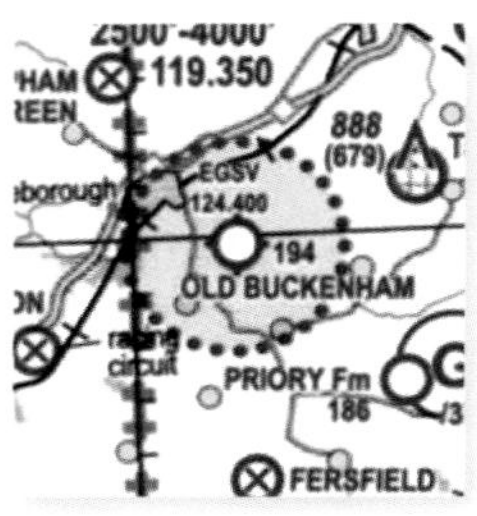

Figure AL11.10
An ATZ surrounding Old Buckenham aerodrome, as depicted on a UK VFR aeronautical chart.

In the UK an **Aerodrome Traffic Zone** (**ATZ**) is airspace surrounding an aerodrome from the surface up to a height of 2000ft above the aerodrome level. The ATZ extends in a circle with a radius of 2 nautical miles from the mid-point of the longest runway. If the longest runway is more than 1850 metres long (or if the ATZ would extend to less than 1.5nm beyond the end of any runway on the aerodrome), the ATZ has a radius of 2.5 nautical miles. If an aerodrome has an ATZ, it will depicted on aeronautical charts (except for airfields wholly within a control zone) and details notified in the UK AIP. An ATZ does not have its own airspace classification, but takes the classification of the airspace it is located within.

EGSV AD 2.17 AIR TRAFFIC SERVICES AIRSPACE

Designation and lateral limits	Vertical Limits	Airspace Class	ATS unit callsign/ language	Transition Altitude	Remarks
1	2	3	4	5	6
OLD BUCKENHAM AERO-DROME TRAFFIC ZONE (ATZ) A circle, 2 nm radius centred at 522951N 0010307E on longest notified runway (07/25)	Upper limit: 2000 ft Lower limit: SFC	G	BUCKENHAM RADIO		

EGSV AD 2.18 AIR TRAFFIC SERVICES COMMUNICATION FACILITIES

Service Designation	Callsign	Channel(s)	Hours of Operation	Remarks
1	2	3	4	5
Other	BUCKENHAM RADIO	124.400 MHz A/G Frequency	Winter: Fri, Sat, Sun 0930-SS and by arrangement. Summer: Fri, Sat, Sun 0930-1800 and by arrangement.	ATZ hours coincident with A/G hours, but not by arrangement.

Figure AL11.11
Details of ATZs are found in the AIP.

An aircraft must not fly, take-off or land within an ATZ except with the permission of the relevant ATC unit, or after obtaining information from the aerodrome's Flight Information Service or Air Ground Communications Service. Whilst within the ATZ the aircraft commander must maintain a continuous 'watch', that is listen out, on the appropriate radio frequency.

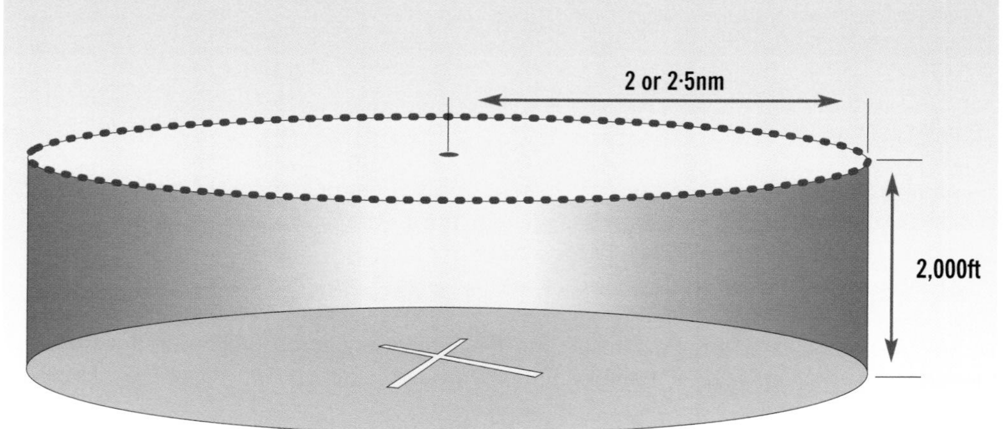

Figure AL11.12
The dimensions of a UK Aerodrome Traffic Zone (ATZ). The horizontal radius is 2nm if centred on a runway with a length of 1850 metres or less, or 2.5nm if centred on a runway longer than 1850nm.

At a Government (eg UK military) aerodrome the ATZ is active during the hours notified in the UK AIP – often 24 hours a day, 7 days a week. At other aerodromes the ATZ is usually active during the 'hours of watch' of the aerodrome's ATC, Flight Information Service or Air Ground Communications Service; these hours are notified in the UK AIP.

Name Lateral Limits Vertical Limits Class of Airspace	Unit Providing Service	Callsign Language Hours of Service, Conditions of Use	Frequency/ Channel Purpose	Remarks
1	2	3	4	5
MARHAM ATZ A circle, 2.5 nm radius centred at 523854N 0003302E on longest notified runway (06/24) Upper limit: 2000 ft Class: G	MARHAM	MARHAM DIRECTOR English H24	124.150 MHz ATC	Elevation: 75 ft. Runway length: 2786 m. Government Aerodrome.

Figure AL11.13
Details of a military (Government) aerodrome ATZ – in this case RAF Marham. Note that the ATZ is active 'H24' – in other words 24 hours a day, 7 days a week.

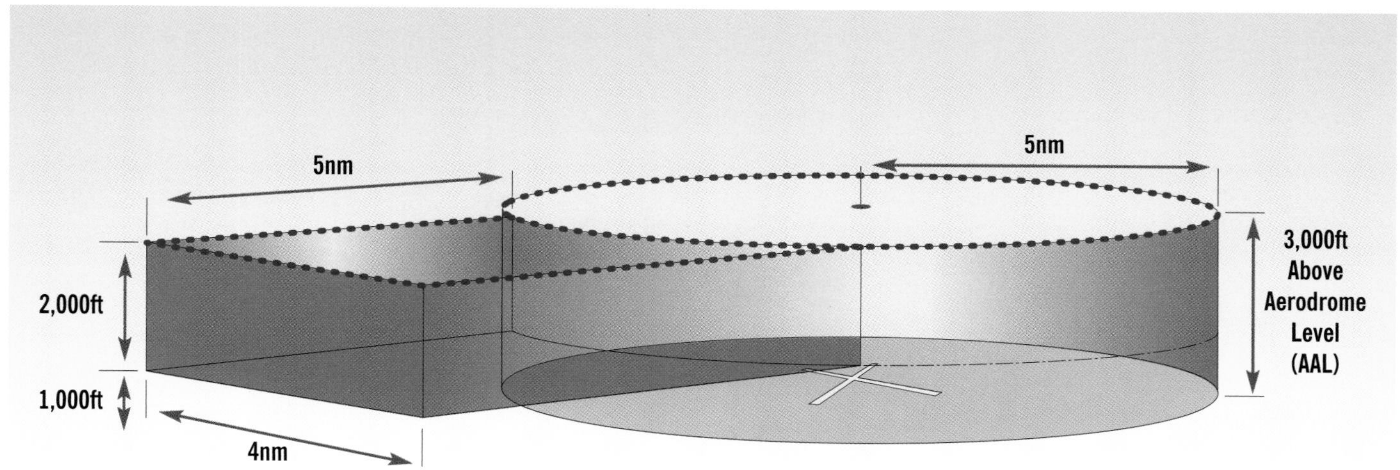

Figure AL11.14
The standard dimensions of a UK MATZ.

Certain UK military aerodromes may additionally be surrounded by a **Military Aerodrome Traffic Zone – MATZ**. A MATZ normally has a radius of 5 nautical miles from the mid-point of the longest runway and extends from the surface to a height of 3000ft above the aerodrome. Additionally there is usually a 'stub', which is a corridor along the extended centre-line of the approach to the main runway, with a width of 4 nautical miles (nm) and extending out by an additional 5nm. The 'stub' of the MATZ has a base of 1000ft above aerodrome level and an upper limit of 3000ft above aerodrome level. MATZs are depicted on aeronautical charts and details are notified in the UK AIP and are normally active whenever the aerodrome is open. A MATZ does not have its own airspace classification, but takes the rules and procedures of the airspace it is located within.

Where two or more MATZ are grouped together the resulting airspace may be known as a Combined Military Aerodrome Traffic Zone (CMATZ) and one aerodrome will be designated as the controlling aerodrome. The upper limit of a CMATZ is set by reference to the highest aerodrome.

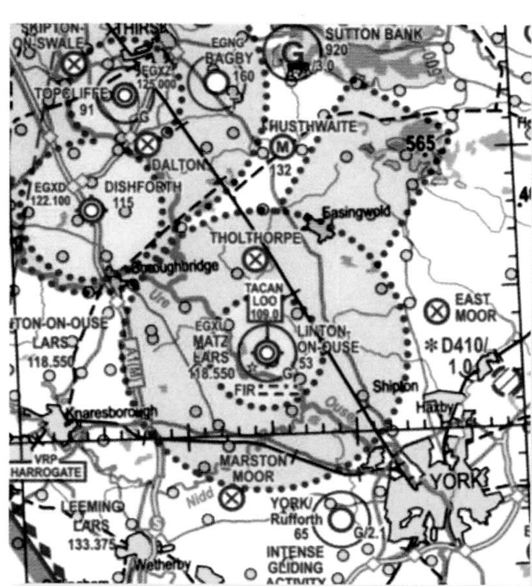

Figure AL11.15
A MATZ (in this case around RAF Linton-on-Ouse) as depicted on a UK VFR aeronautical chart. The aerodrome's ATZ is also depicted.

Figure AL11.16
MATZ help to separate civilian and military aircraft around military airfields.

Pilots planning to cross or operate within a MATZ are strongly recommended to establish two-way contact with the MATZ on the appropriate radio frequency at least 15nm or 5 minutes flying time from the MATZ boundary – whichever is greater. If the MATZ controller cannot offer a crossing service, the pilot is strongly recommended to avoid the MATZ – after all it is there to protect aircraft and in particular to avoid collisions or dangerous encounters between civilian and military aircraft. Furthermore, regardless of the status of a MATZ, the rules in relation to a military aerodrome's ATZ apply independently and as already covered, military ATZs are normally active 24 hours a day, seven days a week.

Visual Meteorological Conditions (VMC) and Visual Flight Rules (VFR)
SERA VMC minima apply in UK airspace, with two exceptions. In Glass G airspace, at or below 3000ft amsl and at or below 140 knots indicated airspeed, the minimum flight visibility for VFR flight is 1,500 metres, whilst remaining clear of cloud and with the surface in sight. In Class D airspace by day only, at and below 3000ft amsl and at or below 140 knots indicated airspeed the minimum conditions for VFR flight in an aeroplane is 5 kilometres flight visibility, clear of cloud and with the surface in sight; in a helicopter 1500 metres flight visibility, clear of cloud and with the surface in sight.

The UK VMC minima are summarised in the table below:

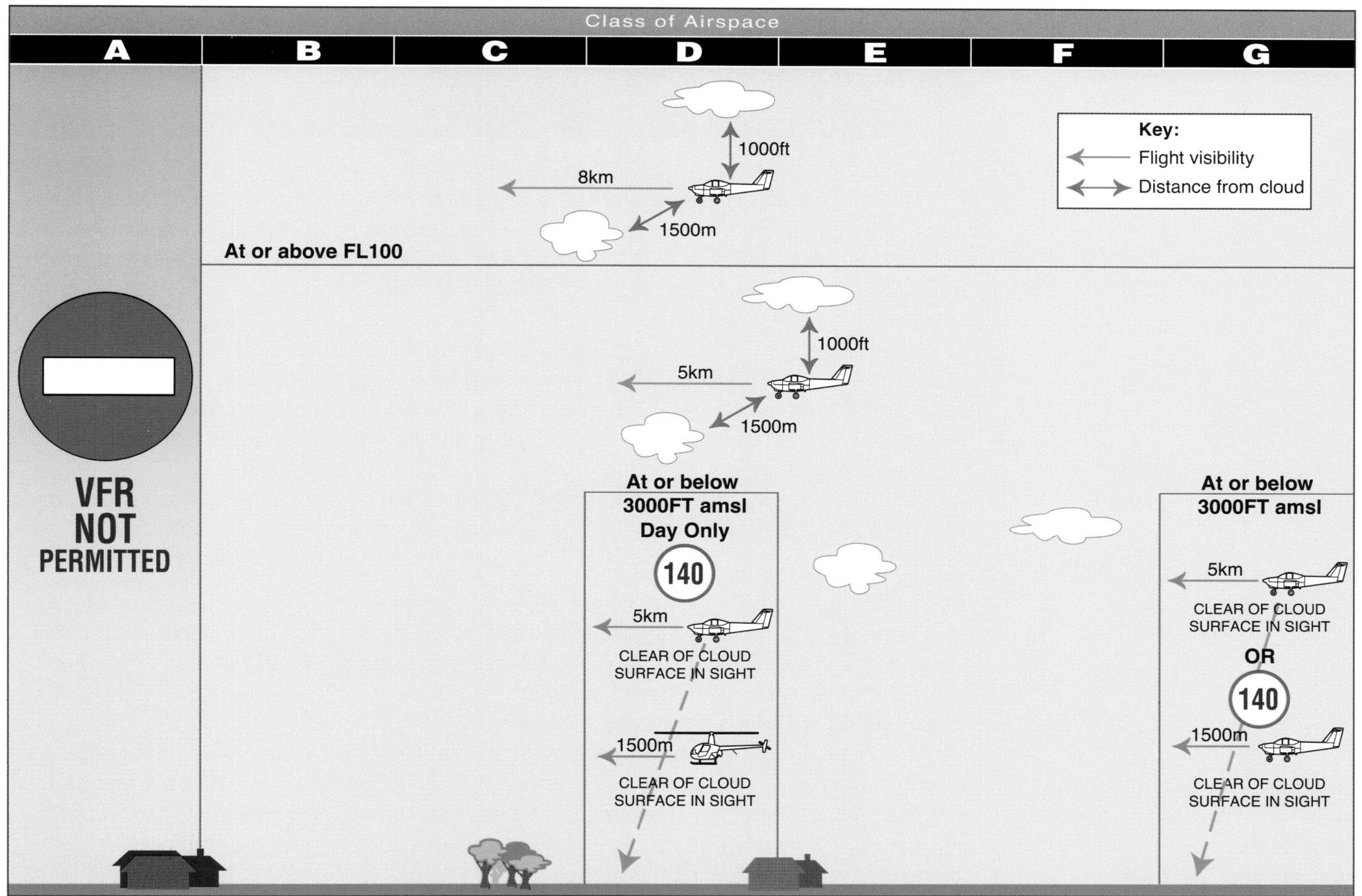

Figure AL11.17
The UK Visual Meteorological Condition (VMC) minima.

The Air Navigation Order (ANO) defines 'with the surface in sight' as meaning that the flight crew are able to see sufficient surface features or surface illumination to maintain the aircraft in a desired attitude without reference to any flight instrument.

The UK CAA permit a VFR flight to use cruising levels different to those specified by SERA in relation to the aircraft's magnetic track, unless otherwise instructed by ATC.

The UK CAA exempts VFR flights from the requirement to fly no lower than 500ft above the surface or obstacles, and instead require that aircraft fly no closer than 500ft to any person, vessel, vehicle or structure.

If an aircraft in the UK wishes to take-off or land within 1,000 metres of an organised open-air assembly of more than 1000 people, it may only do so at an aerodrome and in accordance with procedures notified by the CAA; or at another landing site in accordance with procedures notified by the CAA and with the written permission of the organiser of the assembly.

Figure AL11.18
Under the UK rules of the air, and with certain exceptions, aircraft must fly no closer than 500ft to any person, vessel, vehicle or structure.

In the UK aircraft are exempt from the 500ft and 1000ft low flying rules if practicing approaches to land at an aerodrome, or practising approaches to forced landings other than at an aerodrome, and *"flying in accordance with normal aviation practice."* This exemption permits an aircraft to practice an approach but then make a go-around rather than a landing – for example for training purposes.

Helicopters conducting manoeuvres in accordance with 'normal aviation practice' are exempt the '500ft' rule when within the boundaries of an aerodrome or other 'permitted site' (ie permitted by the CAA). When operating in accordance with this exemption, a helicopter must not fly closer than 60 metres to any person, vessel, vehicle or structure outside the aerodrome.

Aircraft in the UK are exempt from the '1000ft' rule over a congested area if operating on a Special VFR flight when operating in accordance with procedures for a 'notified' route.

Airspace Classifications

Military danger areas in the UK may be subject to byelaws which make unauthorised entry (or trespass) into a military danger a criminal offence. A UK danger area may offer one of two services to aircraft wishing to enter a danger area during its notified hours of activity:

Danger Area Crossing Service (**DACS**); or

Danger Area Activity Information Service (**DAAIS**).

DACS is an in-flight service which can, when the danger area activity permits, provide a clearance to enter the appropriate danger area. Details of DACS will be found in the UK AIP, with the contact frequency depicted on aeronautical charts. It is important to appreciate that a DACS 'clearance' relates to the danger area activity only, and may not provide information or separation from other aircraft or terrain.

Figure AL11.19
Details of UK danger areas, including DACS & DAAIS facilities, are found in the UK AIP.

ENR 5.1 PROHIBITED, RESTRICTED AND DANGER AREAS (continued)

UNITED KINGDOM AIP

A DAAIS is an in-flight service which allows a pilot to obtain an update on the current status of a danger area, the pilot can then use that information to decide whether it is safe to enter the danger area. Details of DAAIS will be found in the UK AIP, with the contact frequency depicted on aeronautical charts.

A temporary danger area may be established in the event of an emergency incident in the UK Flight Information Regions (FIRs), particularly if extensive Search and Rescue (SAR) operations are taking place. Such a temporary danger area will be notified by NOTAM and it should be obvious that flight within a temporary danger area should be avoided by any 'non-participating' aircraft. If a temporary danger area is failing to have the desired effect, or if the emergency or incident is considered sufficiently serious, a temporary restricted area may be established. It is an offence to fly within a designated **Restricted Area** (**Temporary**) without the permission of the appropriate Emergency Controlling Authority (ECA).

Temporary restricted areas with longer notice periods may be established in the UK for major public events and air displays. Details of these airspace restrictions, and associated procedures, will be published well in advance of the event (often in an Aeronautical Information Circular – AIC) and also referred to in NOTAMs.

There are a number of recognised further hazards to flight within UK airspace. Details of Military Training Areas (MTAs); Aerial Tactics Areas (ATAs) and Air-to-Air Refuelling Areas (AARAs) are given in the UK AIP, but as a general rule these activities take place at levels well above those commonly used by VFR flights.

A number of **Areas of Intense Aerial Activity** (**AIAA**) exist in the UK, these are areas where there is an unusually intense concentration of civil and/or military flying activity including 'unusual' manoeuvres such as aerobatics, formation flying, etc. Full details of an AIAA are given in the UK AIP (including the times of 'peak' activity') and they are marked on aeronautical charts together with the appropriate contact radio frequencies. Pilots intending to fly within an AIAA are strongly recommended to make contact on the notified frequency and if possible obtain some form of radar service.

Figure AL11.20
An Area of Intense Aerial Activity (AIAA) depicted on a UK aeronautical chart.

ENR 5.2 MILITARY EXERCISE AND TRAINING AREAS (continued)

Name Lateral Limits	Upper - lower Limit System/means of activation announcement/information for Civil Flights	Remarks and time of activity
1	2	3
AIAA THE WASH AREA 530900N 0001200E - 530900N 0003300E - 530400N 0004800E - 525835N 0004800E - then along the coastline to 524700N 0002232E - 524000N 0002200E - 525206N 0000610W - 525648N 0000949W - 530900N 0001200E	Upper limit: 3500 ft ALT Lower limit: SFC	**Hours:** Peak activity takes place 0900 to 1700 Mon to Thu and 0900 to 1500 Fri Winter (Summer 1hr earlier). **Remarks:** Because of the holding patterns associated with Danger Area EG D207 special caution is advised in the Wash Area. **Advisory Measures:** Pilots are strongly recommended to avoid the area. If this is not possible, a LARS should be requested from: Marham ATC on 124.150 MHz, Coningsby ATC on 120.800 MHz or Waddington ATC on 127.350 MHz
AIAA SHAWBURY 523130N 0030612W - 523702N 0031803W - 525515N 0031726W - 530239N 0030347W - 530445N 0021031W - 525314N 0020227W - 523710N 0021524W - 523212N 0022430W - 523209N 0023708W - 522828N 0024502W - 522828N 0025230W - 523130N 0030612W but excluding Controlled Airspace.	Upper limit: FL70 Lower limit: SFC	**Hours:** Permanently active from 0700 to 0130 Mon to Thu and from 0700 to 1700 Fri Winter (Summer 1hr earlier). **Remarks:** Intense instrument flying and general handling training by large numbers of helicopters (including initial helicopter pilot training), together with IFR fixed wing airfield approaches and departures by student pilots. Night operations may be conducted using reduced navigation and/or anti-collision lights. **Advisory Measures:** Pilots are strongly recommended to avoid this area; if this is not possible a LARS is available from Shawbury ATC on 133.150 MHz.
AIAA OXFORD 515600N 0014900W - 520130N 0011745W - 515745N 0011126W - 514328N 0010000W - 513433N 0010000W - 513423N 0011138W - 513938N 0015510W - 515600N 0014900W	Upper limit: 5000 ft ALT Lower limit: SFC	**Hours:** Permanently active. **Remarks:** There is intense air activity associated with closely woven civil and military climb out and approach procedures for the many airfields in the vicinity. Pilots flying in this area are advised to keep a constant vigilance particularly during weekdays when military activity is at its peak, and especially in the area 8.5 nm/308°(T) and 6 nm/145°(T) from Oxford/Kidlington aerodrome where aircraft may be holding awaiting clearance to join airways. **Advisory Measures:** Radar services are available within this area from Brize Norton ATC on 124.275 MHz. The attention of pilots is also drawn to the Brize Norton Control Zone. (See ENR 2.1).

Figure AL11.21
Details of Areas of Intense Aerial Activity (AIAA) in the UK AIP.

The UK also has **Advisory Radio Areas** (**ARA**) around areas where regular test flying takes place. Details of ARAs are given in the UK AIP and they are noted on aeronautical charts, pilots intending to fly in an ARA are strongly advised to contact to appropriate ATS unit to obtain information on test flying activity.

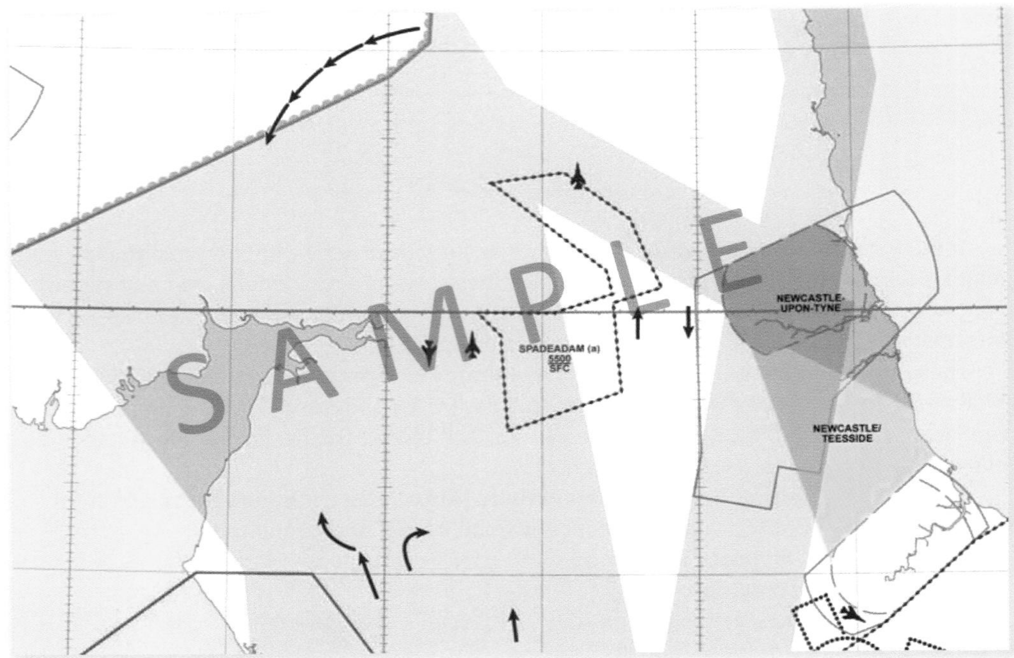

Figure AL11.22
A map within the UK AIP shows areas where regular low level military flying takes place.

In addition to these hazards to flight, military low level flying may take place almost anywhere in the UK outside controlled airspace. Although military 'low flying' is defined as flight below 2000ft above ground level (AGL), the greatest concentration of military low flying takes place between 250ft and 500ft above the surface. A map in the UK AIP indicates general areas and direction of flight for military low level flying, but it must be stressed that low level military aircraft may be found almost anywhere outside controlled airspace and especially in rural and remote areas. Although low flying military aircraft will normally avoid active airfields (for example, those with an ATZ), they may not be aware of smaller or less-active airstrips and flying sites. It is also worth knowing that military aircraft often travel in pairs or larger groups so if you do spot one, look for at least one other in the vicinity.

Figure AL11.23
Low level military flying can take place almost anywhere in the UK outside controlled airspace.

Other activities of a dangerous nature exist within UK airspace. **Small arms ranges**, where live ammunition is fired, may not attract danger area status if they are not a hazard above 500ft AGL. These small arms ranges are listed in the UK AIP and not surprisingly pilots are advised to avoid these areas if flying below 500ft AGL.

The UK Met Office regularly releases hydrogen or helium balloons (typically about 1.5 metres in diameter) from a number of sites in the UK. These balloons carry a radio transmitter (radiosonde) which makes atmospheric measurements as the balloon rises – they can reach over 80,000ft. Details of launch sites are given in the UK AIP.

There are a small number of permanent sites where powerful lasers may be emitted into airspace, these are marked on UK aeronautical charts and details are given in the UK AIP, they usually have no safe upper limit and so the vertical extent is given on aeronautical charts as 'UNL' – unlimited.

Figure AL11.24
Tacolneston High Intensity Radio Transmission Area (HIRTA) as marked on an aeronautical chart, extending from the surface to 3,300ft AMSL as indicated by the figure '3.3'.

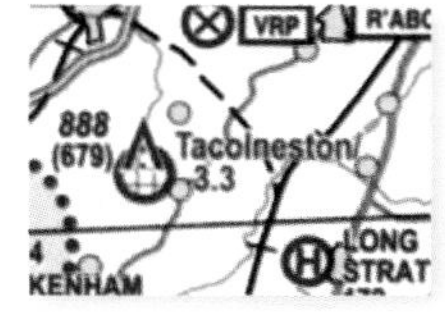

High Intensity Radio Transmission Areas (**HIRTA**) are areas of airspace within which there may be intense radio energy which can cause interference with, or even damage to, aircraft communications and navigation equipment. HIRTAs are marked on aeronautical charts (including their upper limit in thousands of feet AMSL) and details listed in the UK AIP, which states that the intensity of radio energy may be sufficient to detonate electrically initiated explosive devices carried or fitted in aircraft. The UK AIP also says that in some HIRTAs the radio energy may be so intense that remaining for more than one minute in the immediate vicinity of the energy source is a health hazard which may cause injury or harm.

The UK also has a number of **Gas Venting Sites** (**GVS**) over which severe turbulence and even power fluctuations in turbine engines may be experienced when methane gas is released under high pressure. A GVS is marked on UK aeronautical charts with its upper limit in thousands of feet above mean sea level; details are also given in the UK AIP.

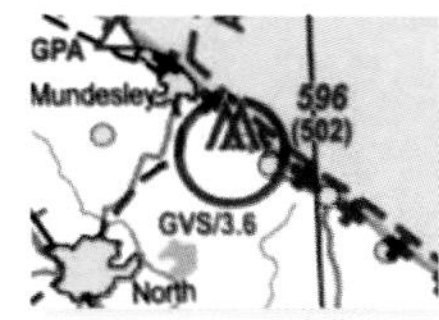

Figure AL11.25
A Gas Venting Station (GVS) as marked on an aeronautical chart, extending from the surface to 3,600ft AMSL as indicated by the figure '3.6'.

On occasion temporary controlled airspace (sometimes abbreviated to CAS-T) may be established in the UK for the benefit of **Royal Flights** – aircraft carrying a member of the UK Royal Family or a head of state. Where possible Royal Flights using 'fixed wing' aircraft fly in existing controlled airspace, but where necessary temporary controlled airspace is established including temporary control areas and temporary control zones around an airfield. Such temporary controlled airspace will be classified as Class D and the appropriate access restrictions (in particular the requirement to obtain ATC permission to enter the airspace) apply. Details of Royal Flights and any associated temporary controlled airspace (CAS-T) are given in NOTAMs.

Temporary controlled airspace (CAS-T) is not normally established for Royal Flights using helicopters in uncontrolled airspace, which instead operate within a **Royal Low Level Corridor** (**RLLC**). An RLLC is marked by a series of check points or waypoints and military aircraft are required to avoid a protected area which is 5 nautical miles either side of the helicopter's intended track and from the surface to 1000ft above the helicopter's maximum intended cruise altitude. Civilian flights are highly recommended to avoid an RLLC and keep well away from a Royal Flight helicopter.

Figure AL11.26
A Sikorsky S-76C helicopter of the UK 'Royal Flight'.

Within UK airspace, the CAA have established a policy that any aircraft wishing to operate within a **Radio Mandatory Zone** (**RMZ**) must establish two-way radio communiation with the appropriate ATC unit before entering the RMZ, by passing the information required under SERA. The CAA policy is quite specific that if the answer to an initial call from the aircraft is an ATC instruction to *"Standby"*, before the required information has been passed to ATC and acknowledged, the aircraft must remain outside the RMZ. In aviation radio communications *"Standby"* means 'Wait and I will call you'. No clearance or approval is granted by the phrase *"Standby"*.

Altimeter Setting Procedures

Altimeter Setting Procedures in UK airspace are detailed in the UK AIP. The default Transition Altitude within the UK is 3000ft, except within or beneath certain areas of controlled airspace where a different transition altitude may be specified and noted in the AIP. In general a VFR flight operating outside controlled airspace can use any desired altimeter setting and VFR flights operating above 3000ft amsl in UK airspace are <u>not</u> required to fly at the appropriate level in relation to the aircraft's magnetic track as stated in SERA, unless required to do so by ATC.

The UK is divided into a number of **Altimeter Setting Regions** (**ASR**) and within each ASR a **Regional Pressure Setting** (**RPS**) will be forecast. A Regional Pressure Setting is the lowest QNH forecast to occur within the ASR for each hour. Any ATC unit should be able to supply the current RPS for its ASR, and probably the RPS for the next hour as well. The stated purpose of a RPS is to make up for any lack of stations reporting their own QNH, which might be the case in remote areas where reporting stations are few and far between. Nevertheless, when flying below controlled airspace, pilots are recommended to use the QNH of an adjacent aerodrome.

ENR 1.7-2 | **UNITED KINGDOM AIP**
4 Feb 2016

ENR 1.7 ALTIMETER SETTING PROCEDURES (continued)

4 Selected Transition Altitudes

4.1 The following Transition Altitudes apply to flights within or beneath the following Airspace:

Airspace	Transition Altitude
Aberdeen CTR/CTA	6000 ft
Belfast CTR/TMA	6000 ft
Birmingham CTR/CTA	6000 ft
Bristol CTR/CTA	6000 ft
Cardiff CTR/CTA	6000 ft
Channel Islands CTR/CTA	5000 ft
Clacton CTA	6000 ft
Daventry CTA	6000 ft
Doncaster Sheffield CTR/CTA	5000 ft
Durham Tees Valley CTR/CTA	6000 ft †
East Midlands CTR/CTA	6000 ft
Edinburgh CTR/CTA	6000 ft
Glasgow CTR/CTA	6000 ft
Leeds Bradford CTR/CTA	5000 ft †
Liverpool CTR/CTA	5000 ft
London TMA	6000 ft
Manchester TMA	5000 ft
Newcastle CTR/CTA	6000 ft
Norwich CTR/CTA	5000 ft †
Portsmouth CTA	6000 ft
Scottish TMA	6000 ft
Solent CTA	6000 ft †
Sumburgh CTR/CTA	6000 ft †
Worthing CTA	6000 ft

Note: *† Outside the notified hours of operation the Transition Altitude is 3000 ft*

5 Detailed Procedures

5.1 **Take-off and climb**

5.1.1 A QNH altimeter setting is given with the taxiing clearance prior to take-off.

5.1.2 At UK aerodromes the designated location for pre-flight altimeter checks is the apron.

5.1.3 For all major UK aerodromes, the apron elevation (or the elevation of various parts of an apron where there is significant variation between them) has been determined and the value is displayed in the flight clearance office at the aerodrome concerned. It is also given at AD 2.8.

5.1.4 Within Controlled Airspace a pilot should set one altimeter to the latest Aerodrome QNH prior to take-off. While flying at, or below, the Transition Altitude vertical position will be expressed in terms of altitude based upon the Aerodrome QNH. When cleared for climb to a Flight Level, vertical position will be expressed in terms of Flight Level, unless intermediate altitude reports have been specifically requested by Air Traffic Control.

5.1.5 Outside Controlled Airspace, a pilot may use any desired setting for take-off and climb. However, when under IFR, vertical position must be expressed in terms of Flight Level on climbing through the Transition Altitude.

5.1.6 Pilots taking-off at aerodromes beneath Terminal Control Areas and Control Areas should use aerodrome QNH when flying below the Transition Altitude and beneath these Areas, except that the aerodrome QFE may be used when flying within the circuit. It may be assumed that for aerodromes beneath the same TMA or CTA the differences in their QNH values are insignificant.

5.2 **En-route**

5.2.1 **Within Controlled Airspace**

5.2.1.1 At and above the transition level and during en-route flight the aircraft should be flown at Flight Levels. The latest and most appropriate Regional Pressure Setting value is to be used for checking terrain clearance in flight. Aircraft flying in a Control Zone or TMA at an Altitude at or below the Transition Altitude will be given the appropriate QNH setting in their clearance to enter the Zone/TMA.

5.2.2 **Outside Controlled Airspace and within Active TRAs**

AMDT 2/2016 | **CIVIL AVIATION AUTHORITY**

Figure AL11.27
UK altimeter setting procedures are set out in the UK AIP, including areas where a 'non-standard' transition altitude applies.

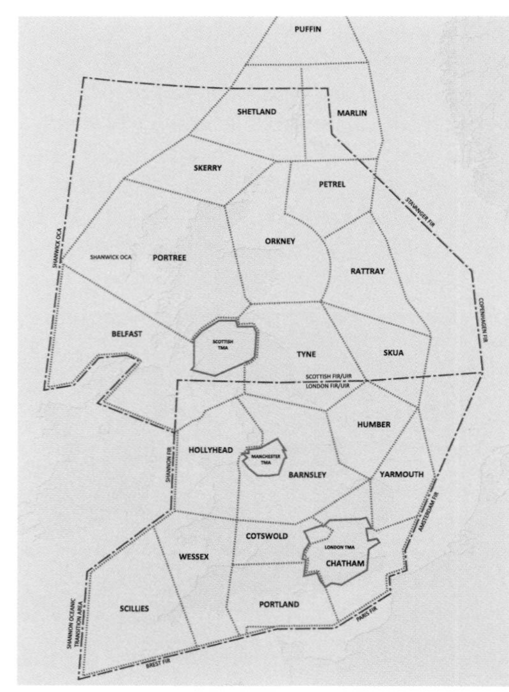

Figure AL11.28
The altimeter setting regions of the UK.

Figure AL11.29
A typical Air Ground Communications Service (AGCS) unit at a UK airfield.

Air Traffic Services

As an alternative to ATC or AFIS facilities, in the UK an airfield may have an **Air Ground Communication Service** (**AGCS**) – also sometimes abbreviated to A/G. AGCS radio station operators provide traffic and weather information to pilots operating on and in the vicinity of an airfield. Traffic information in particular may be based primarily on reports made by other pilots. Information provided by an AGCS radio station operator is intended to assist pilots, but an AGCS cannot issue clearances or instructions and cannot be certain of knowing all traffic in the area. In practice, because the AGCS may be provided by someone who has other duties on the airfield, it is not unknown to find there is no AGCS operator to speak to even during the notified hours of operation. In this case there may be other pilots on frequency who can provide basic aerodrome information (runway in use, QNH etc) and details of any known traffic.

EGPT AD 2.18 AIR TRAFFIC SERVICES COMMUNICATION FACILITIES

Service Designation	Callsign	Channel(s)	Hours of Operation	Remarks
1	2	3	4	5
Other	PERTH RADIO	119.800 MHz Service Designation: A/ G.	Winter 0900 - 1700 Summer 0800 - 1600	ATZ hours coincident with A/G hours.

Figure AL11.30
Details of the Air Ground Communications Service (A/G) service at Perth aerodrome, as listed in the UK AIP.

An AGCS is indicated by a call sign using the airfield name and the word *"Radio"*. For example 'Perth Radio' indicates an AGCS at Perth airfield. The notified hours of an AGCS (sometimes abbreviated to 'A/G'), its call sign and frequency will be given at the appropriate aerodrome entry in the 'Aerodrome' section of the UK AIP.

An Air Ground Communication Service does <u>not</u> provide an alerting service.

Aeronautical Information Service (AIS)
The UK Aeronautical Information Service is operated by behalf of the Civil Aviation Authority by National Air Traffic Services (NATS). The UK AIP is arranged in accordance with ICAO annex 15 and at the time of writing it is available in hard-copy (printed) version, CD-ROM and on-line via the NATS aeronautical information service website.

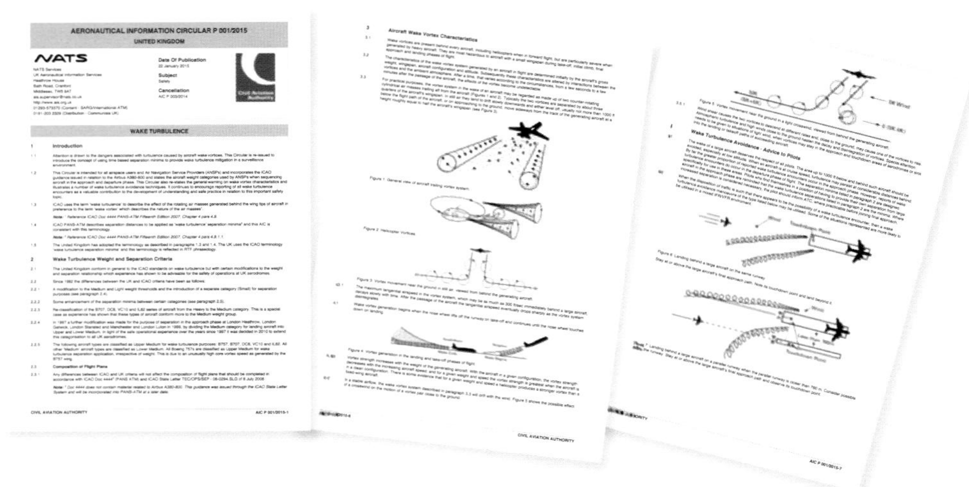
AERONAUTICAL INFORMATION CIRCULAR P 001/2015
UNITED KINGDOM
NATS
WAKE TURBULENCE

Figure AL11.31
An Aeronautical Information Circular (AIC), accessible via the UK AIS website.

A part of the UK integrated AIP package is a series of **Aeronautical Information Circulars** which the UK CAA uses to publish a wide variety of safety and administration information. The UK AIC series is colour-coded to indicate the nature of the AIC. That colour system is:

Pink	Safety related information and advice.
Yellow	Operational matters.
Mauve	UK Airspace Restrictions under Restriction of Flying Regulations – mostly air displays and major public events.
Green	Maps and Charts.
White	Administrative matters (examination dates, licensing issues etc).

The UK AIS website is the official UK source of AIS information and also the access point for NOTAMs. To check NOTAMs it is necessary to register on the website (there is no fee for this service), the user can then access NOTAMs in the form of **Pre-flight Information Bulletins** (**PIB**) which can be defined in a number of ways, including:

Aerodrome Brief	A PIB containing NOTAMs for the selected aerodrome(s).
Area Brief	A PIB containing FIR and Aerodrome NOTAMs for the selected Flight Information Region(s).
Point Brief	A PIB containing FIR NOTAMs affecting a specified circle from an aerodrome, navigation aid or Lat/Long co-ordinate.
VFR FIR Brief – EGTT	A PIB containing all FIR and Aerodrome NOTAMs for the London FIR (ICAO code EGTT). The briefing is sorted in order North to South.
VFR FIR Brief – EGPX	A PIB containing all FIR and Aerodrome NOTAMs for the Scottish FIR (ICAO code EGPX). The briefing is sorted in order North to South.
Narrow Route Brief	Probably the most popular form of PIB. The user selects departure, destination and alternate airfields, route, maximum level and flight rules. A PIB is created for a user-specified corridor along the route.

Pre-Flight Information Bulletin

- Bulletin generated: 2016/10/17 05:56 UTC
- Report reference no: **400000006045740**

UK Aeronautical Information Service (NATS)
Website: www.ais.org.uk
Email: eg_notamprop@ead.eurocontrol.int
UK AIS Telephone: +44 (0)1489 612488

- Period: 2016/10/17 05:56 UTC TO 2016/10/17 17:56 UTC
- Flight Rules: **VFR** (lower: 000, upper: 050)
- PIB includes **NOTAM**

- Adep: **EGMC**
- Ades: **EGPT**
- FIR: **EGTT EGPX**

- Route: F050 DCT DCT
- Width: +/-5NM

En-Route Information
EGTT: LONDON FIR

Q) EGTT/QSPLT/IV/BO/AE/000/031/5403N00115W005
A) EGXU B) FROM: 16/03/18 09:47C) TO: 16/05/31 17:00 U0851/16
E) LINTON ON OUSE PRIMARY RADAR COVERAGE LIMITED TO 45NM UP TO FL170

Q) EGTT/QSPLT/IV/BO/AE/000/003/5310N00031W005
A) EGXW B) FROM: 16/03/21 08:44C) TO: 16/06/20 23:59 U0880/16
E) ALL APPROACH AIDS FOR WADDINGTON UNAVAILABLE DUE TO RUNWAY REBUILD.

Q) EGTT/QSELT/IV/B/E/000/090/5310N00031W030
B) FROM: 16/04/28 15:41C) TO: 16/07/25 08:00
E) WADDINGTON LOWER AIRSPACE RADAR SERVICE ONLY AVBL FM SURFACE LEVEL TO 9000FT AMSL. B0691/16

Q) EGTT/QSEAU/IV/B/E/000/100/5306N00010W030
B) FROM: 16/05/16 07:00C) TO: 16/05/19 11:00
E) CONINGSBY LOWER AIRSPACE RADAR SERVICE UNAVAILABLE B0767/16
SCHEDULE: 0700-1100

Q) EGTT/QOBCE/IV/M/AE/000/004/5302N00031W001
A) EGYD B) FROM: 16/03/14 12:16C) TO: 16/05/22 17:00
E) CRANE OPR WI 0.055NM RADIUS OF 530153N 0003048W (RAF CRANWELL), U0768/16
MAX HGT 121FT AGL/340FT AMSL

Q) EGTT/QAFXX/IV/NBO/E/000/999/5248N00149W999
B) FROM: 16/03/23 08:12C) TO: PERM
E) DELETE ENTRY FOR CROSS HAYES GLIDER SITE, STAFFORDSHIRE B0434/16
UK AIP ENR 5.5 REFERS

Figure AL11.32
A sample 'Narrow Route' Pre-flight Information Bulletin generated by the UK AIS website.

Although many UK airfields have good internet access for pilots, meaning that NOTAMs can be checked immediately before flight, the UK AIS also provides a freephone number at which a recorded message can be accessed. This message contains information supplementing that found in the PIBs and in particular provides up-to-date information on restricted areas (for example, Red Arrows displays); airspace upgrades (such as Royal Flights in fixed wing aircraft) and emergency restrictions of flying (to prohibit flight in the vicinity of a major incident).

Information is recorded after the last upgrade and/or Restriction of Flying for the current day, or at 1900 UTC, whichever is earlier and is updated during the day should any change or addition be required.

The relevant contact phone numbers are given in the AIP and flight guides, but at the time of writing are:

UK 0500 354802 International +44 (0)20 8750 3939

Pilot Licensing

Under UK law, it is a criminal offence for any person to act as flight crew or perform an 'aviation function' when the **proportion of alcohol** in his or her breath, blood or urine exceeds the prescribed limit. Those limits are:

- in the case of breath, 9 microgrammes of alcohol in 100 millilitres;
- in the case of blood, 20 milligrammes of alcohol in 100 millilitres;
- in the case of urine, 27 milligrammes of alcohol in 100 millilitres.

For reference, these limits are approximately one quarter of the comparable limits for driving in England, Wales and Northern Ireland.

Regulations concerning UK-specific pilot licences are contained within the UK Air Navigation Order (ANO).

In addition to EASA pilot licences, in the UK it is possible to obtain a **National Private Pilot Licence** (**NPPL**). The UK National Private Pilot Licence (NPPL) is a licence issued by the UK CAA that is valid in UK airspace for the piloting of UK registered aircraft only, although it may be used in another country with the permission of the relevant authorities of that country. Depending upon the class ratings included in the NPPL it may be used to fly microlight aeroplanes, Self-Launching Motor Gliders (SLMG), helicopters and/or 'Simple Single Engine Aeroplanes' (SSEA).

The holder of a National Private Pilot's Licence is not required to hold a medical certificate. Instead, a NPPL holder can make a 'declaration' to the UK CAA that he or she reasonably believes that they:

- meet the medical requirements for a Group 1 Licence issued by the Driver and Vehicle Licensing Agency; and
- are not subject to a 'disqualifying medical condition'.

In the case of a licence holder aged 70 years or more, this a declaration must have been made within the previous three years.

A 'disqualifying medical condition' means any physical or mental condition or illness, or any history of such a condition or illness, including:

- any alcohol or drug abuse, addiction or misuse;
- any neurological condition;
- any functional disability;
- any surgery or medical treatment;
- any collapse, fainting or loss of consciousness;
- such other medical conditions as the CAA may specify, that might *"impair the safe operation of normal flight controls or render the licence holder unfit at any time to perform any function for which the licence is granted."*

A declaration ceases to be valid if it is withdrawn; and must be withdrawn by the holder if they no longer reasonably believe that they satisfy the requirements. It may also be withdrawn by the CAA if it has reason to believe that the holder no longer meets the medical requirements or has a disqualifying medical condition.

The holder of an NPPL who does not have a medical certificate and relies on a medical 'self-declaration' can only exercise the privileges of the licence:

- in an aircraft with a maximum take-off mass of 5,700kg or less;
- with not more than three passengers on board;
- by day or when exercising the privileges of a night rating;
- in visual meteorological conditions; and
- within the United Kingdom unless the holder has the permission of the competent authority for the airspace in which the aircraft is being flown.

A licence holder wishing to exercise night rating privileges must additionally meet the colour vision requirements of 'MED.B.075 of Part-MED'.

Incidentally, a medical declaration can also be used by the holder of a 'legacy' UK Private Pilot Licence, but not the holder of an EASA licence.

The holder of a UK NPPL(A) with an SSEA/SLMG rating may fly non-EASA SSEA or SLMGs, registered in the UK, within UK airspace.

A **Simple Single Engine Aeroplane** (**SSEA**) is a single engine aeroplane which has a maximum take-off weight of not more than 2000kg.

The key elements of the training course for an NPPL (SSEA or SLMG) are to:

- complete at least 32 hours flight time as pilot of aeroplanes (excluding Navigation Skill Test and General Skill Test). This flight time must include at least 22 hours of dual flight instruction and 10 hours of supervised solo flight time. The solo flight time must include at least 4 hours of solo cross-country flight time.
- Successfully complete at least 1 solo cross-country flight of at least 100 nautical miles, during which full stop landings are made at 2 aerodromes different from the aerodrome of departure.
- Pass examination(s) on the theoretical knowledge subjects of air law, operational procedures, communications, meteorology, navigation, principles of flight, flight performance and planning, aircraft general knowledge and human performance.
- Pass a Navigation Skill Test (NST) – a minimum of 1 hour duration and to be taken prior to undertaking the qualifying solo cross-country flight.
- Pass a General Skill Test (GST) – a minimum of 1 hour duration.

The minimum age for holding an NPPL is 17 years, there is no maximum age.

An NPPL holder may not fly any aeroplane for the purpose of commercial air transport, public transport or aerial work, except under very specific circumstances for towing aircraft and giving flight instruction or testing.

The NPPL can carry passengers, but may not fly as pilot in command of any aeroplane if the total number of people carried (including the pilot) exceeds four. In relation to the '90 day' currency rule for carrying passengers, the holder of an NPPL is exempt from this requirement if the only passenger carried is a single passenger who is qualified to act as pilot in command for the intended flight. Before flight, the passenger must be informed of the pilot's lack of 90 day recency and the roles of passenger and PIC must be clearly agreed before the flight.

An NPPL holder must not operate under IFR. The holder of an NPPL for helicopters must not fly at night.

The holder of an SSEA rating must complete differences training before flying as PIC on an aeroplane which has:

- a tricycle undercarriage;
- a tailwheel;
- a supercharger or turbo-charger;
- a variable pitch propeller;
- retractable undercarriage;
- cabin pressurisation system; or
- a maximum continuous cruising speed in excess of 140 knots indicated airspeed.

Any required differences training must be given by a flight instructor, recorded in the holder's personal flying logbook and endorsed and signed by the instructor conducting the training.

An SSEA or SLMG class rating is valid for 24 months. To revalidate an SSEA or SLMG class rating attached to an NPPL(A), the holder must, during the validity of the current certificate of revalidation for the rating:

Pass a General skill test;

or

Complete at least 12 hours flight time to include at least 8 hours as pilot in command; at least 12 take-offs and 12 landings; at least 1 hour of flying training with an instructor and at least 6 hours flight time in the 12 months preceding the expiry of the class rating.

If an NPPL holder wishes to revalidate more than one class rating he or she may carry out the requirements above in any of the relevant classes, but must have at least 1 hour PIC or 1 hour dual instruction in each of the other classes as part of the 12 hours flight time.

Figure AL11.33
The practical exam for the grant of a Flight Radiotelephony Operator's Licence (FRTOL) can be taken at many locations throughout the UK.

Other than class ratings, only a night rating can be added to a NPPL(A).

With the exception of pilots undergoing flight training (that is, a student pilot), an aircraft radio must only be operated by a person who is 'duly licensed'. This means that the operator must hold a **Flight Radiotelephony Operator's Licence** (**FRTOL**). To be granted an FRTOL an applicant must be at least 16 years old, have passed a theoretical knowledge exam and practical test and have demonstrated a level of language proficiency acceptable to the CAA. Although the FRTOL can be granted as a 'standalone' licence, it is more normally issued in conjunction with another flight crew licence.

A personal flying logbook must be retained for at least two years after the date of the last entry in it, and during that period it must be produced to an 'authorised person' within a reasonable time of being requested. An **authorised person** includes the police and a person authorised by the UK CAA. In practice, most pilots keep their flying logbook(s) for life as they soon become the only complete record of a pilot's flights.

UK regulations concerning UK-specific pilot licences are contained in Schedule 8 of the Air Navigation Order (ANO). The ANO also contains general rules regarding the conduct of UK-certified pilots and operation of UK-certified or UK-permit aircraft. Many of these rules are, in practice, quite similar to the appropriate EU/EASA regulation. Nevertheless, Appendix 2 contains a summary of some specific provisions of the ANO.

Progress Check

109 What organisation is the 'Competent Authority' for the UK?
110 How is a 'congested area' defined?
111 At a UK aerodrome, can an aircraft land on a runway if there is already another aircraft on the runway?
112 What is the meaning of the following aerodrome marking?

113 Assuming a UK aerodrome has a single runway 1000m long, what would be the appropriate ATZ dimensions?
114 What are the standard dimensions of a UK MATZ?
115 Away from a congested area or open air assembly, what is the minimum height or separation for a VFR flight?
116 Where will a pilot find details of DACS and DAAIS?
117 What are the general criteria for an AIAA?
118 On a UK aeronautical chart, what is indicated by a small circle marked 'GVS 2.9' ?
119 What is the primary requirement of a flight wishing to enter a UK RMZ?
120 What service is provided by a station using the call sign "*Radio*"?
121 What is the definition of an SSEA?
122 What is the maximum number of passengers who can be flown by a NPPL?
123 What qualification must a UK pilot hold in order to operate the aircraft radio?
124 For what period must a UK pilot retain their personal flying logbook?

These questions are intended to test knowledge and reinforce some of the key learning points from this section. In answering these questions, a 'pass rate' of around 80% should be the target.

Model answers are found at page 148

AL Progress Test Answers

AL1 International Aviation Law

AL2 European Rules of the Air

AL3 Aerodromes

AL4 Visual Meteorological Conditions (VMC) and Visual Flight Rules (VFR)

AL5 Airspace Classifications

AL6 Altimeter Setting Procedures

AL7 Air Traffic Services

AL8 Aeronautical Information Service (AIS)

AL9 Urgency and Distress Procedures

AL10 Pilot Licensing

AL11 National Procedures

AL Progress Test Answers

AL1 International Aviation Law

1. For ICAO Standards and Recommended Practices (SARP) to become legally binding they have to be made into law in a specific country (or group of countries – for example the EU). In practice, most countries base their aviation laws and procedures on ICAO SARP and where a country has rules or procedures that differ significantly from an ICAO standard, the state will usually publish a list of those 'differences'.
2. Explanations for 'Implementing Regulations', which form EU law, are published by EASA in the form of Acceptable Means of Compliance and Guidance Material (AMC/GM). AMC/GM give detail and guidance about how aviation law should be applied in practice.
3. A competent authority is the authority designated by an EU member state as competent to ensure compliance with the requirements of an EU regulation. In practice, the competent authority is the national aviation authority in a country.

AL2 European Rules of the Air

4. The Pilot-In-Command is the pilot designated by the aircraft operator or owner as being in command and charged with the safe conduct of a flight.
5. In relation to the rules of the air, the PIC "*may depart from these rules in circumstances that render such departure absolutely necessary in the interests of safety.*"
6. The PIC is responsible for all pre-flight actions and the PIC must consider "*...all available information appropriate to the intended operation*" before flight.
7. If two aircraft are approaching 'head-on' (or approximately 'head-on') and there is a danger of collision, each aircraft must alter its heading <u>to the right.</u>
8. If two aircraft of the same class are converging, the aircraft that has the other to its right must give way – "*On the Right, In the Right*".
9. If an aircraft wishes to overtake another aircraft in the air, the aircraft that is being overtaken has right of way and the overtaking aircraft must alter its heading <u>to the right</u> to keep clear.
10. An overtaking situation exists whilst the overtaking aircraft is at an angle of 70° or less to the centreline of the aircraft being overtaken.
11. The arriving aircraft must observe other aerodrome traffic to avoid collision and conform with the traffic pattern formed by other aircraft.
12. When two or more 'heavier-than-air' aircraft are approaching to land, the higher aircraft must give way to the lower aircraft. However, an aircraft at the lower level must not cut in front of another aircraft which is in the final stages of an approach to land, or overtake that aircraft. If a pilot is aware that another aircraft is making an emergency landing, that pilot must give way to the emergency aircraft.
13. When two aircraft on the ground are approaching head on, or approximately so, each shall <u>stop</u> or where practicable alter its course <u>to the right</u> to keep well clear.

14. When two aircraft on the ground are on a converging course, the one which has the other on its right shall give way – *"On the right, in the right"*.
15. An aircraft which is being overtaken by another aircraft on the ground shall have the right-of-way, the overtaking aircraft shall keep well clear of the other aircraft.
16. An aircraft taxiing on the manoeuvring area must stop and hold at all lighted stop bars and may only proceed past that point in accordance with an ATC clearance, when the lights are switched off. Therefore an aircraft can only cross a lit stop bar if *"...absolutely necessary in the interests of safety."*
17. An aircraft taxiing on the manoeuvring area of a controlled aerodrome must stop and hold at all runway-holding positions, unless an explicit clearance to enter or cross the runway has been issued by ATC.
18. An aeroplane can only be taxied on the movement area of an aerodrome if the person at the controls is an appropriately qualified pilot; or has been designated by the operator.

AL3 Aerodromes

19. A taxiway designator, in this case denoting taxiway 'B' or 'Bravo'.
20. A runway holding position, the broken lines are on the 'runway' side of the position.
21. This is a mandatory 'No Entry' sign
22. A white cross designated a runway or taxiway (or section of runway or taxiway) unfit for the movement of aircraft.
23. This marking denotes a 'displaced' runway threshold – an aircraft must not land on the area marked by the white arrows, but may use that area for take-off.
24. Slightly low
25. An incursion 'hot spot'. A 'hot spot' is a zone or area on the airfield in which incursions have taken place, or in which there is an increased risk of incursion.
26. The 'C' indicates the place where pilots can report to the Air Traffic Services Unit at an airfield. In practice it is the place where pilots can pay any landing fees, obtain airfield information etc.
27. The long shaft of the 'T' is parallel to the direction of take-off and landing.
28. The aerodrome boundary, or areas on an aerodrome that are unfit for the movement of aircraft.
29. Stop (the speed of movement of the arms indicates the required rate of coming to a halt).
30. Identify gate (This indicates the parking area, stand or gate the aircraft is being marshalled to).
31. Land
32. Recommend stop.
33. The pilot can indicate ready to start engine(s) by holding up a single finger (for starting a single engine, or engine number one) and a number of fingers to indicate the number of the engine to be started.
34. Give way to other aircraft and continue circling.

AL4 Visual Meteorological Conditions (VMC) and Visual Flight Rules (VFR)

35. Flight visibility at least 5 kilometres and a distance of at least 1500 meters horizontally and 1000ft vertically from cloud.
36. 'Flight visibility' means the visibility forward from the cockpit of an aircraft in flight.
37. Cloud ceiling not less than 1,500ft and ground visibility not less than 5km.
38. Flight visibility not less than 1500m.
39. Flight visibility not less than 800m (for helicopters only).
40. Classes A, B, C & D.
41. If ATC offer pilot a clearance which is not satisfactory, or is unsafe, or which the pilot cannot comply with, the pilot-in-command must inform ATC that the clearance is not acceptable.
42. On a magnetic track of between 000° – 179°, a VFR flight should choose a cruising level of 'Odd' thousands + 500 – eg altitude 5,500ft; FL75 etc.
43. An aircraft must not fly over the 'congested area' of a city, town or settlement, nor over an open-air assembly of people, unless it is high enough so that in an emergency it can make a landing without 'undue hazard' to persons and property on the surface. A VFR flight is subject to an absolute minimum height of not less than 1000ft above the highest obstacle within a 600 metre radius of the aircraft when flying over a congested area, or open air assembly.
44. A VFR flight must not fly lower than 500ft above the surface, nor less than 500ft above the highest obstacle within 150 metres (500ft) of the aircraft.

AL5 Airspace Classifications

45. Controlled airspace may be class A, B, C, D or E.
46. Airspace within which an air traffic control service is provided is Controlled Airspace.
47. A VFR flight wishing to operate in A, B, C & D airspace must obtain ATC clearance to enter, maintain continuous communications with ATC and accept an ATC service.
48. A CTA is a 'control area', that is controlled airspace extending upwards from a specified level above the earth to a specified upper limit.
49. A CTR is a 'control zone', that is controlled airspace extending upwards from the surface of the earth to a specified upper limit.
50. NO – VFR flight is not permitted in Class A airspace.
51. A Restricted area - airspace of defined dimensions, within which the flight of aircraft is restricted in accordance with certain specified conditions.
52. Full details of a danger area will be found in the relevant Aeronautical Information Publication (AIP).
53. An 'ATZ' is an 'Aerodrome Traffic Zone' - a flight wishing to operate within an ATZ is required to make contact with the Air Traffic Service at the aerodrome.
54. Class G is the least restrictive class of uncontrolled airspace, sometimes known as the 'open FIR'.
55. An 'RMZ' is a 'Radio Mandatory Zone' - airspace within which *"...the carriage and operation of radio equipment is mandatory"*.

56. The carriage and operation of a pressure-altitude reporting transponder is mandatory in a TMZ – 'Transponder Mandatory Zone'.

AL6 Altimeter Setting Procedures

57. An altimeter measures air pressure.
58. An 'altitude' is a vertical distance 'above mean sea level' (amsl).
59. When moving from an area of high pressure to an area of low pressure, any given pressure level will move closer to the surface. Thus, an aircraft following a constant pressure level will come lower – "High to low, down you go".
60. QFE pressure setting means that the altimeter is indicating "height" above a specific point on the surface, usually an aerodrome.
61. An 'elevation' of 330ft means that the airfield is 330ft above sea level. 330 divided by 30 (feet per hectopascal) means that 330ft is equivalent to 11hPa. Airfield QNH will be greater than airfield QFE (because the airfield is above sea level), so QFE of 1003hPa, + 11hPa, equates to an airfield QNH of 1014hPa.
62. A VFR flight cruising below the Transitional Altitude, and below a CTA, should use an altimeter setting of the QNH of an airfield beneath the CTA.
63. The Transition Level is the lowest useable Flight Level above the transition altitude.
64. The Standard Pressure altimeter setting is 1013hPa.
65. At Flight Level 55, the aircraft is at 5,500ft above the 1013hPa pressure level. The difference between 1013 and the QNH given (1003hPa) is 10hPa, which at 30ft per hPa equates to 300ft.

When the altimeter pressure setting is reduced (wound down), indicated level also reduces. As the QNH (1003) is less than the Standard Pressure (1013), the aircraft's altitude is 300ft lower than its Flight Level, ie 5,200ft.

66. On a magnetic track of 270°, above the Transition Level an aircraft in VFR cruising flight must operate at 'even' Flight Levels + 500ft – eg FL65, FL85 etc.

The difference between QNH (995hPa) and Standard Pressure (1013hPa) is 18hPa, which at 30ft per hPa equates to 540ft.

If the Transitional Altitude is 5000ft, the lowest 'even +500' Flight Level is FL65. At FL65, the aircraft's altitude is 540ft lower, thus 5,960ft. This altitude is still above the stated Transition Altitude of 5000ft, and so FL65 is the lowest Flight Level to use by a VFR flight on the given magnetic track.

AL7 Air Traffic Services

67. A 'controlled' aerodrome is an airfield at which an ATC service is provided.
68. ATIS means 'Automatic Terminal Information Service' - a recorded radio broadcast of airfield and meteorological information for departing and arriving flights.
69. An 'approach control service' is an ATC service for 'controlled flights' arriving and departing at an airfield.
70. Full information on ATC services can be found in the Aeronautical Information Publication (AIP).
71. A 'Flight Information Service' provides *"...advice and information useful for the safe and efficient conduct of flights"* – it is not a control service.

72. A Flight Information Region (FIR) is the region within which a state will provide a flight information service.
73. An Aerodrome Flight Information Service is a Flight Information Service provided at a specific airfield.
74. Any flight receiving an air traffic control service, or a flight information service, is also receiving an alerting service.

AL8 Aeronautical Information Service (AIS)

75. Information on specific airfields will be found in the AERODROMES (AD) section of an AIP.
76. AIRAC (**A**eronautical **I**nformation **R**egulation **A**nd **C**ontrol) is a regular amendment cycle for providing advance notification of permanent and operationally significant changes to the AIP.
77. A NOTAM contains information or warnings which are too temporary, or too urgent, for inclusion within the normal system of updating and amending the AIP.
78. These figures indicate that the NOTAM is valid from 11:07 UTC on the 5th April 2016 to 23:59UTC on the 4th July 2016.
79. The Aerodrome Traffic Zone (ATZ) at Carlisle aerodrome has been deactivated. Air Traffic Service is not available and the aerodrome is not available to aircraft, except those which have 'out-of-hours' permission.

AL9 Urgency and Distress Procedures

80. The words 'Pan Pan' indicate an 'Urgency' situation.
81. The word 'Mayday' indicates a 'Distress' situation.
82. Repeatedly switching the landing light(s) on and off and/or repeated irregular switching of the navigation lights on and off indicates that the aircraft is compelled to land, but does not require immediate assistance.
83. A distress situation is "*...a condition of being threatened by serious and/or imminent danger and requiring immediate assistance.*"
84. The transponder code 7700 indicates an emergency situation.
85. The transponder code 7600 indicates a radio failure.
86. An intercepted aircraft should attempt to establish contact with the intercepting aircraft on the international VHF emergency frequency of 121.5MHz.
87. You have been intercepted, follow me.
88. If any instructions received from ATC conflict with those given by the intercepting aircraft, the intercepted aircraft should request immediate clarification while continuing to comply with the instructions given by the intercepting aircraft.

AL10 Pilot Licensing

89. 60 months
90. The pilot must not fly and must seek advice from an Aero-Medical Examiner (AME) without delay.
91. The pilot must not fly and must seek advice from an Aero-Medical Examiner (AME) without delay.

92. Except in very specific circumstances, a PPL is prohibited from flying in return for remuneration – that is receiving money or some other valuable compensation, otherwise known as 'hire or reward' or 'valuable consideration'.
93. The time from the moment an aircraft first moves for the purpose of taking off, until the moment it finally comes to rest at the end of the flight.
94. The time from the moment a helicopter's rotor blades start turning until the moment the helicopter finally comes to rest at the end of the flight, and the rotor blades are stopped.
95. Flight time during which the student pilot is the sole occupant of the aircraft.
96. In order to carry passengers a pilot must have carried out, in the preceding 90 days, at least 3 take-offs, approaches and landings in an aircraft of the same type or class, or a Full Flight Simulator (FFS) representing that type or class.
97. No
98. No
99. Circumstances that might give cause for limiting, suspending or revoking a pilot's licence include:
    - Obtaining the pilot licence by falsification of submitted documentary evidence;
    - Falsification of logbook and licence records;
    - The licence holder no longer complies with the applicable requirements of Part-FCL;
    - Exercising the privileges of a licence when adversely affected by alcohol or drugs;
    - Non-compliance with the applicable operational requirements;
    - Evidence of malpractice or fraudulent use of the licence.
100. The minimum medical standard for holding a LAPL is a LAPL medical certificate.
101. A maximum certificated take-off mass of 2000kg or less.
102. A maximum of 3 passengers, so that there are never more than 4 persons on board the aircraft.
103. Differences training - the acquisition of additional knowledge and training on an appropriate training device or the aircraft.
104. Familiarisation training is the acquisition of additional knowledge.
105. Single engine, single pilot class ratings are valid for a period of 24 months.
106. To revalidate an SEP or TMG class rating, the pilot can:
    - Pass a proficiency check in the appropriate aeroplane class within 3 months of the expiry date of the rating;
      OR
    - Within the 12 months preceding the expiry of the rating, complete at least 12 hours of flight time in the relevant aeroplane class, including at least 6 hours as PIC and 12 take-offs and landings. Additionally, complete a training flight of at least 1 hour with a flight instructor (FI) or a class rating instructor (CRI). The training flight is not required if a pilot has completed a class or type rating 'proficiency check' or skill test in any other class or type of aeroplane.
107. A type rating is valid for 12 months.
108. Yes – an aerobatic rating.

AL11 National Procedures

109. The UK Civil Aviation Authority
110. In relation to a city, town or settlement, 'Congested Area' means any area which is substantially used for residential, industrial, commercial or recreational purposes.
111. In the UK, a 'flying machine' or glider must not land on a runway at an aerodrome if there is another aircraft on the runway, unless authorised to do so by an ATC unit.
112. An area of a UK aerodrome which must be used only for the taking off and landing of helicopters.
113. From the surface up to a height of 2000ft above the aerodrome level, in a circle with a radius of 2 nautical miles from the mid-point of the longest runway. If the ATZ would extend to less than 1.5nm beyond the end of any runway on the aerodrome, the ATZ will have a radius of 2.5 nautical miles.
114. A UK MATZ normally has a radius of 5 nautical miles from the mid-point of the longest runway and extends from the surface to a height of 3000ft above the aerodrome. Additionally there is usually a 'stub' which is a corridor along the extended centre-line of the approach to the main runway, with a width of 4 nautical miles (nm) and extending out 5nm from the edge of the MATXZ 'circle'. The 'stub' of the MATZ has a base of 1000ft above aerodrome level and an upper limit of 3000ft above aerodrome level.
115. An aircraft on a VFR flight in the UK is required to fly no <u>closer</u> than 500ft to any person, vessel, vehicle or structure.
116. In the UK Aeronautical Information Publication (AIP).
117. Areas of Intense Aerial Activity (AIAA) in the UK are areas where there is an unusually intense concentration of civil and/or military flying activity including 'unusual' manoeuvres such as aerobatics, formation flying, etc.
118. A Gas Venting Site (GVS), with an upper limit of 2,900ft amsl.
119. Any aircraft wishing to operate within a UK Radio Mandatory Zone (RMZ) must establish two-way radio communication with the appropriate ATC unit before entering the RMZ.
120. An 'Air Ground Communication Service' (AGCS), sometimes abbreviated to 'A/G'.
121. A Simple Single Engine Aeroplane (SSEA) is a single engine aeroplane which has a maximum take-off weight of not more than 2000kg.
122. There is no specific limitation of how many passengers a NPPL may carry.
123. A Flight Radiotelephony Operator's Licence (FRTOL).
124. A personal flying logbook must be retained for at least two years after the date of the last entry in it. In practice, most pilots keep their flying logbook(s) for life as they soon become the only complete record of a pilot's flights.

Appendix 1 – Abbreviations

Aviation has an unfortunate habit of using hundreds of abbreviations, some more comprehensible than others. Here is a list of common aviation abbreviations used in this publication:

A/G	Air / Ground
AAL	Above Aerodrome Level
AARA	Air-to-Air Refuelling Area
AD	AERODROMES (section of AIP)
AFIS	Aerodrome Flight Information Service
AGCS	Air Ground Communication Service
AGL	Above Ground Level
AIAA	Area of Intense Aerial Activity
AIC	Aeronautical Information Circular
AIP	Aeronautical Information Publication
AIRAC	Aeronautical Information Regulation And Control
AIS	Aeronautical Information Service
AMC/GM	Acceptable Means of Compliance and Guidance Material
AME	Aero-Medical Examiner
AMSL	Above Mean Sea Level
ANO	Air Navigation Order
APAPI	Abbreviated Precision Approach Path Indicator
ARA	Advisory Radio Area
ASFC	Above Surface
ASR	Altimeter Setting Region
ATA	Aerial Tactics Area
ATC	Air Traffic Control
ATIS	Automatic Terminal Information Service
ATS	Air Traffic Service
ATSU	Air Traffic Service Unit
ATZ	Aerodrome Traffic Zone
BPL	Balloon Pilot Licence
C	Centre
CAA	Civil Aviation Authority'

CAS-T	Temporary Controlled Airspace
CMATZ	Combined Military Aerodrome Traffic Zone
CRI	Class Rating Instructor
CTA	Control Area
CTR	Control Zone
DAAIS	Danger Area Activity Information Service
DACS	Danger Area Crossing Service
EASA	European Aviation Safety Agency
ECA	Emergency Controlling Authority
EFIS	Electronic Flight Instrument System
EIR	En-route Instrument Rating
ENR	EN-ROUTE (section of AIP)
EU	European Union
FCL	Flight Crew Licencing
FFS	Full Flight Simulator
FI	Flight Instructor
FIR	Flight Information Region
FIS	Flight Information Service
FL	Flight Level
FNPT	Flight and Navigation Procedures Trainer
FRTOL	Flight Radiotelephony Operator's Licence
FSTD	Flight Simulation Training Device
GA	General Aviation
GEN	GENERAL (section of AIP)
GMP	General Medical Practitioner
GST	General Skill Test
GVS	Gas Venting Site
HIRTA	High Intensity Radio Transmission Area
hPa	Hectopascal
HPA	High Performance Aeroplane
ICAO	International Civil Aviation Organisation
IFR	Instrument Flight Rules

ILS	Instrument Landing System
IMC	Instrument Meteorological Conditions
IR	Instrument Rating
L	Left
LAPL	Light Aircraft Pilot Licence
LFA	Local Flying Area
LFZ	Local Flying Zone
MATZ	Military Aerodrome Traffic Zone
MEP	Multi engine Piston
MP	Multi Pilot
MTA	Military Training Area
NAA	National Aviation Authority
NATS	National Air Traffic Services
NPPL	National Private Pilot Licence
NST	Navigation Skill Test
P	Cabin pressurisation
PAPI	Precision Approach Path Indicator
PIB	Pre-flight Information Bulletin
PIC	Pilot In Command
PPL	Private Pilot Licence
PPR	Prior Permission Required
R	Right
RLLC	Royal Low Level Corridor
RMZ	Radio Mandatory Zone
RPS	Regional Pressure Setting
RU	Retractable undercarriage
SAR	Search and Rescue
SARPs	Standards and Recommended Practices
SEP	Single-Engine Piston
SERA	Standardised European Rules of the Air
SET	Single Engine Turbo-prop
SLMG	Self Launching Motor Glider

SP	Single Pilot
SPL	Sailplane Pilot Licence
SPLC	Single Lever Power Control
SSEA	Simple Single Engine Aeroplane
SSR	Secondary Surveillance Radar
SUP	Supplement (section of AIP)
T	Turbo or super-charged engines
TMA	Terminal Manoeuvring Area
TMG	Touring Motor Glider
TMZ	Transponder Mandatory Zone
TW	Tail wheel
UIR	Upper Information Region
UK	United Kingdom
UTC	Co-ordinated Universal Time
VASI	Visual Approach Slope Indicator
VFR	Visual Flight Rules
VMC	Visual Meteorological Conditions
VP	Variable pitch propeller
XPDR	Transponder

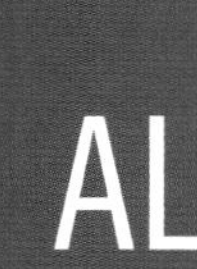

Appendix 2 – Specific provisions of the 2016 UK Air Navigation Order (ANO)

The 2016 UK Air Navigation Order (ANO) is a piece of UK legislation which deals principally with rules and procedures for aircraft with a UK ('National') Certificate of Airworthiness or Permit to Fly, and pilots with UK-specific licences such as a National Private Pilot Licence (NPPL). Many of the provisions of the ANO are, for practical purposes, very similar to the equivalent EU / EASA legislation. Nevertheless, the following is a summary of some specific ANO provisions which relate to non-commercial, VFR flight:

Responsibilities and authority of the pilot in command

The pilot in command of an aircraft is responsible:

- for defining the roles and duties of each crew member before every flight;
- for the operation and safety of the aircraft and for the initiation, continuation, termination or diversion of a flight in the interest of safety; and
- for ensuring the safety of all crew members, passengers and cargo on board during aircraft operations.

The more detailed provisions of the ANO regarding the obligations of the pilot in command are covered under the 'Operational Procedures' section of the Theoretical Knowledge syllabus.

Pilot to remain at controls and be secured in seat

During flight, the pilot in command must:

- keep any safety belt fastened while at the pilot's station; and
- remain at the controls of the aircraft at all times except if another pilot is taking the controls.

A helicopter rotor must not be turned under power for the purpose of making a flight unless there is a person at the controls entitled to act as pilot in command of the helicopter.

Operation of radio in aircraft

A radio in an aircraft must not be operated (whether or not the aircraft is in flight), except:

- in accordance with the conditions of the licence issued for that radio; and
- by a person licensed or otherwise permitted to operate the radio.

The radio in an aircraft must not be operated in a way that could cause interference with the efficiency of aeronautical telecommunications or navigational services.

Dropping of articles and animals

Articles and animals (whether or not attached to a parachute) must not be dropped, or permitted to drop, from an aircraft in flight in a way that could endanger persons or property. Further provisions apply to parachuting operations.

Grant of United Kingdom flight crew licences

The CAA (or a person approved by the CAA) will grant licences specified in Part 1 of Schedule 8 of the ANO, authorising the holder to act as a member of the flight crew of a non-EASA aircraft registered in the United Kingdom, if it is satisfied that the applicant is:

- a fit person to hold the licence; and
- is qualified by having the knowledge, experience, competence, skill and physical and mental fitness to act in the capacity to which the licence relates.

A licence granted under this legislation is not valid unless it has been signed by the holder in ink or an indelible pencil.

A licence granted under this legislation remains in force for the period indicated on the licence, not exceeding the period specified in Part 1 of Schedule 8 of the ANO. If no period is indicated on the licence, it remains in force for the lifetime of the holder.

Licence holder not fly when unfit

A person must not act as a member of the flight crew of an aircraft registered in the United Kingdom if they know or suspect their physical or mental condition renders them temporarily or permanently unfit to perform such functions, including unfitness by reason of:

- injury or sickness;
- taking or using any prescribed or non-prescribed medication which is likely to interfere with the ability to perform such functions;
- receiving any medical, surgical or other treatment that is likely to interfere with the ability to perform such functions;
- the effects of any psychoactive substance; or
- fatigue.

Every holder of a medical certificate or medical declaration who:

- suffers any personal injury involving incapacity to undertake the holder's functions;
- suffers any significant illness involving incapacity to undertake those functions throughout a period of 21 days or more; or
- in the case of a woman, has reason to believe that she is pregnant;
- must inform an aeromedical examiner authorised by the CAA of such injury, illness or pregnancy, as soon as possible in the case of injury or pregnancy, and as soon as the period of 21 days has expired in the case of illness.

The medical certificate or declaration is suspended upon the occurrence of such injury or the expiry of such period of illness or the confirmation of the pregnancy.

In the case of injury or illness the suspension ceases when:

- the holder is medically assessed under arrangements made by the CAA and pronounced fit to resume the holder's functions; or
- the CAA exempts the holder from the requirement of a medical assessment.

In the case of pregnancy, the suspension:

- may be lifted by the CAA or an aeromedical examiner for such period and subject to such conditions as the CAA or the aeromedical examiner thinks fit; and
- ceases upon the holder being medically assessed under arrangements made by the CAA after the pregnancy has ended and pronounced fit to resume her functions as a member of the flight crew.

Pilot not to fly after failing a test

The holder of a licence who fails a test, is not entitled to fly in the capacity for which that test would have qualified the holder had it been passed (unless and until the test is re-taken and passed).

Personal flying log

A personal flying log must be kept by every member of the flight crew of an aircraft registered in the United Kingdom; and every person flying for the purpose of qualifying for the grant, renewal or revalidation of a flight crew licence or certificate, whether it is a UK-specific licence or a 'Part FCL' licence.

Production of documents and records

The pilot in command of an aircraft must produce, within a reasonable time after being requested to do so by an authorised person:

- the certificates of registration and airworthiness for the aircraft;
- the licences of its flight crew; and
- any other documents which the aircraft is required to carry when in flight.

The holder of a licence, or a medical certificate, or of a medical declaration, must produce it within a reasonable time after being requested to do so by an authorised person.

An "*authorised person*" generally means a policeman or policewoman or any person authorised by the CAA.

Additional provisions apply to the production of documents by the operator of an aircraft.

Endangering the safety of an aircraft

A person must not recklessly or negligently act in a manner likely to endanger an aircraft, or any person in an aircraft.

Endangering the safety of any person or property

A person must not recklessly or negligently cause or permit an aircraft to endanger any person or property.

Drunkenness in aircraft

A person must not enter any aircraft when drunk, or be drunk in any aircraft.

A person must not, when acting as a member of the crew, be under the influence of drink or a drug to such an extent that their capacity to act as a member of the crew is impaired.

Smoking in aircraft

A person must not smoke in an aircraft registered in the United Kingdom when smoking is prohibited by a notice to that effect.

Authority of the pilot in command

Every person in an aircraft must obey all lawful commands which the pilot in command of that aircraft may give for the purpose of securing the safety of the aircraft and of persons or property carried in the aircraft; or the safety, efficiency or regularity of air navigation.

Acting in a disruptive manner

A person must not, while in an aircraft:

- use any threatening, abusive or insulting words towards a member of the crew of the aircraft;
- behave in a threatening, abusive, insulting or disorderly manner towards a member of the crew of the aircraft; or
- intentionally interfere with the performance of crew member's duties.

Prohibitions in relation to documents and records

A person must not, with intent to deceive:

- use any certificate, licence, approval, permission, exemption or other document which has been forged, altered, revoked or suspended, or to which the person is not entitled;
- nor lend any certificate, licence, approval, permission, exemption or any other document, or allow it to be used by, any other person; or
- make any false representation for the purpose of obtaining the grant, issue, renewal or variation of any such certificate, licence, approval, permission, exemption or other document;
- nor make any false representation in connection with a declaration to the CAA.

A person must not intentionally damage, alter or make illegible any log book or other record required to be maintained; or any entry made in such a log book or record.

A person must not knowingly make, nor assist in the making of, any false entry in or material omission from any log book or record, nor destroy any such log book or record during the period for which it is required to be preserved.

All entries made in writing in any log book or record must be made in ink or indelible pencil.

Obstruction of persons

A person must not intentionally obstruct or impede any person who is exercising a power or performing a duty under the ANO or under an EASA Regulation.

Recent Experience

The holder of a licence must not operate an aircraft carrying passengers as pilot in command or co-pilot unless the holder has carried out, in the preceding 90 days, at least three take-offs, approaches and landings as the sole manipulator of the controls of an aircraft of the same type or class or a full flight simulator representing that type or class. There is an exception to this rule if the intended flight will carry a single passenger who is also qualified to act as pilot in command on that flight; and the holder of the licence has informed the intended passenger that the holder does not meet the recent experience condition.

Cost sharing

A flight can be considered to be a 'non-commercial flight' if the only 'valuable consideration' given or promised for the flight is a contribution to the direct costs of the flight which would be otherwise payable by the pilot in command. The main conditions are that:

- no more than four persons (including the pilot) are to be carried;
- the proportion which the contribution bears to the direct costs must be not more than the proportion which the number of persons carried on the flight (excluding the pilot) bears to the number of persons carried (including the pilot);
- no information has been published or advertised before the flight other than (in the case of an aircraft operated by a flying club), advertising wholly within the premises of the flying club - in which case all the persons carried on such a flight who are aged 18 years or over must be members of that flying club; and
- no person acting as a pilot is employed as a pilot by, or is a party to a contract for the provision of services as a pilot with, the operator of the aircraft being flown.

ANO Definitions:

'Cross-country flight' means a flight between a point of departure and a point of arrival following a pre-planned route, using standard navigation procedures.

'Day' means the time from half an hour before sunrise until half an hour after sunset (both times exclusive), as determined at surface level.

'Flying Machine' means an aeroplane, a powered lift tilt rotor aircraft, a SLMG, a helicopter or a gyroplane.

'Night' means the time from half an hour after sunset until half an hour before sunrise (both times inclusive), as determined at surface level.

'SSEA' means a simple single engine aeroplane - a single engine piston aeroplane with a maximum take-off weight authorised of not more than 2,000kg and which is not a microlight aeroplane or a SLMG.

'With the surface in sight' means with the flight crew being able to see sufficient surface features or surface illumination to enable the flight crew to maintain the aircraft in a desired attitude without reference to any flight instrument.

Appendix 3 – Supplementary Study Material

This publication is designed to provide the knowledge required to understand air law for non-commercial flight operations under Visual Flight Rules (VFR), it is based on the 2015 EASA PPL and LAPL Theoretical Knowledge (TK) Air Law syllabi.

Where a National Aviation Authority (NAA) or training organisation is still working to the 2011 version of the EASA PPL and LAPL Air Law syllabus, there are a small number of topics which are now covered under different TK subjects. If you are preparing for an EASA PPL or LAPL examination under the 2011 syllabus, you are recommended to learn the following supplementary study material, which is presented here in summary form.

Airworthiness of Aircraft (ICAO Annex 8)

A **Certificate of Airworthiness** may be invalidated if an aircraft is repaired or modified in some way which is not approved, if the aircraft is operated outside the operating limits prescribed in the Pilot's Operating Handbook / Flight Manual (POH/FM), or if the aircraft is not maintained in accordance with an approved maintenance schedule.

An aircraft's C of A is normally required to be carried on board an aircraft making an international flight.

Aircraft Nationality and Registration (ICAO Annex 7)

The state of registry is the state on whose register an aircraft is entered.

ICAO recommendation that the **Certificate of Registration** should be carried in the aircraft at all times.

Air Traffic Management (ICAO Annex 11)

The objectives of Air Traffic Services are to:

- Prevent collisions between aircraft
- Prevent collisions between aircraft on the manoeuvring area and obstructions on that area
- Expedite and maintain an orderly flow of air traffic
- Provide advice and information of the safe and efficient conduct of flights
- Notify organisations of aircraft in need of search and rescue aid, and assist such organisations

Security (ICAO Annex 17)

The primary objective of each contracting ICAO state is to safeguard passengers, ground personnel and flight crew, as well as the general public, against any acts of unlawful interference.

Each contracting state should have an organization that is responsible for organizing its practices, procedures and the development and implementation of regulations to safe guard against unlawful interference.

This organisation:

- protects the safety of its crew both on the ground and in the air as well as safeguards the general public as well from acts of unlawful interference.
- is able to respond quickly to any increases in security threat.

Accident and Incident Investigation (ICAO Annex 13)

ICAO definition: *The sole objective of the investigation of an accident or incident shall be the prevention of accidents and incidents. It is not the purpose of this activity to apportion blame or liability.*

An accident is an occurrence associated with the operation of an aircraft which takes place between the time any person boards the aircraft with the intention of flight until such time as all such persons have left the aircraft, in which:

1.) A person is fatally or seriously injured as a result of being in the aircraft, or by direct contact with any part of the aircraft, including parts which have become detached from the aircraft.
2.) The aircraft sustains damage or structural failure which adversely affects the structural strength, performance or flight characteristics of the aircraft, and would normally require major repair or replacement.
3.) The aircraft is missing or is completely inaccessible.

The 'State of Occurrence' must institute an investigation into the circumstances of an accident. The State of Occurrence is defined as the state in the territory of which an accident or incident occurs.

AL Index